Birth stories for the soul

Tales from women, families and childbirth professionals

Birth stories for the soul

Tales from women, families and childbirth professionals

Edited by

Denis Walsh and Sheena Byrom

QUAY
BOOKS

A division of MA Healthcare Ltd

Quay Books Division, MA Healthcare Ltd, St Jude's Church, Dulwich Road, London
SE24 0PB

British Library Cataloguing-in-Publication Data
A catalogue record is available for this book

© MA Healthcare Limited 2009
ISBN-10: 1-85642-357-3; ISBN-13: 978-1-85642-357-1

Printed by CLE, Huntingdon, Cambridgeshire

Contents

Acknowledgements

We would like to thank from the bottom of our hearts all those who have offered and written down their stories in this collection. Mothers, fathers, siblings, grandmothers, midwives and obstetricians from the United Kingdom, Sweden, the USA, Australia and New Zealand have contributed.

We are sure your narratives will connect with and inspire all who read this book.

In some cases names have been changed to protect the authors' anonymity.

Denis Walsh
Midwife and Associate Professor in Midwifery,
University of Nottingham

Sheena Byrom
Midwife and Consultant Midwife
East Lancashire Hospitals NHS Trust and
University of Central Lancashire

CHAPTER I

The power of birth stories

Denis Walsh

Consider the difference between these two accounts of a birth: the first a clinical summary, the second a narrative account by the midwife.

Clinical summary

The woman was a 40-year-old primip with a history of multiple sclerosis that had debilitated her since her early teens. She had hardly worked in that time and suffered intermittently from muscle weakness, although she was mobile with a stick. Her pregnancy was uneventful and she was considering a homebirth. She was a not a good candidate for this given her age, illness and the fact that she was nulliparous. She went into labour and progressed well in the first stage. However the second stage was over two hours, outside of the normal parameters, and constituted a reason for hospital transfer. The attending midwife did not take this option and eventually she delivered. In fact there were no untoward clinical sequelae and she had an unremarkable puerperium.

Narrative account

Sally was a friend I had met through a book club. She had suffered from multiple sclerosis for over 20 years, during which time she was unemployed, although she was highly qualified. I lost touch with her when I moved to another part of the city but had heard that she had married in her late 30s. Then, out of the blue, I got a phone call from her to say that she was pregnant and asking about maternity services. I was working as midwife teacher and had begun to develop a small personal caseload. I enthusiastically agreed to take her onto the caseload. Sally was thinking about a home waterbirth which I was very happy to support her with, although she was 40 and still suffered with multiple sclerosis whose main symptoms were intermittent muscle weakness and fatigue. The obstetrician did not raise any objections, although I knew he was pessimistic that the labour would be straightforward.

I did all the antenatal care at Sally's home and observed over the course of the pregnancy a remission in her symptoms of MS. She was genuinely excited about the baby and birth and went into labour on a bright sunny morning in July.

After a reasonably quick first stage and a tiring two hour second stage, she gave birth to a robust baby girl in the pool. It was a magical moment. The conservatory doors to the garden were open, the sun was streaming through and we could hear children playing in the adjacent neighbour's garden during the labour. She did not lack muscle power during the labour, pushed with great gusto and her and Bill were ecstatic at the birth. She was a confident, instinctive mother. I remember driving home after the birth, feeling proud and elated that I had facilitated a birth that I am sure would have been interventionist in a maternity hospital. In the late 1990s, an elderly primigravida with a history of a chronic, debilitating condition would not have been seen as a good candidate for a homebirth.

For me, it was the realisation of an ideal regarding what being a midwife was all about: personalised, supportive, empathic care for a woman according to her needs and her choices. I had not witnessed a medical event, I had witnessed one of nature's marvels – human childbirth in the perfect setting. She had done it and I was the privileged bystander. To this day, I understand her experience as a healing one. The tentative, introspective woman she was at the beginning of pregnancy grew into a strong, confident mother. She had gone on a transformatory journey and it was beautiful to witness.'

These accounts of the same birth could have come from different planets such is the contrast in content and meaning conveyed. Juxtaposing them in this way dramatically reveals the poverty of the clinical summary as a vehicle for recording the childbirth event. Yet, the first version and thousands like it are much more likely to be held as the official account of events, especially in clinical review settings or where complaints and litigation are being considered. It highlights the need to grant legitimacy to other versions of the same event so that the full context is understood and the perspectives of the principal players are heard. Kirkham (1997), among others, has long argued for a more balanced, humane, interesting and informative account of birth to be recorded alongside the medical account in the maternity record.

Childbirth is replete with human drama and emotion where adversity and triumph walk hand in hand in what Callister (2004) refers to as the 'bittersweet paradox'. In her analysis of a cross-cultural study of women's birth narratives, she found women constantly referring to this paradox. Although the experience is solitary in one sense, women also spoke of the importance of connection with their birth companions who loved them through the experience. It is this combination of challenge and reward played out against a backdrop of human relationships of nurture and compassion that make childbirth narratives so compelling.

In this book, we attempt to capture these narratives from a number of different contexts with a number of different personal perspectives. Our hope is that the 'human dimension' of childbirth will be made visible in these stories and act as a corrector to the bias of the clinical record. It is stating the obvious to say that behind every recorded observation, every clinical measurement, every medical procedure is a unique person with a life history that will never be replicated. That person is about to give birth to a baby who is in turn a unique individual. Giving birth may be a medical event when viewed from within the biomedical paradigm but it is also one of the most amazing, creative and powerful of all human acts. The following chapters attempt to capture something of the richness and variety of these dimensions.

The power of narrative stretches way beyond childbirth and is having something of a renaissance in the broader research literature in health and social care. Roche and Sadowsky (2003) summarise the perennial appeal of the story by noting four reasons for its power:

- Its universality, crossing boundaries of language, culture and age.
- The fact that humans think in narrative structures and the hearing of stories imprints naturally into the mind and memory.
- The stories we tell ourselves help form our identity.
- Stories build and preserve a group's sense of community.

In book shops across the world, the two non-fiction genres that have had remarkable success over the past 15 years are those following the format of '*Chicken Soup for the Soul*' and the 'childhood abuse narratives'. Our book is loosely based on the former's template. The first book in the series, *Chicken Soup for the Soul*, was published in 1993 (Canfield and Hansen, 1993) and became an international publishing phenomenon. The format was short stories of inspiration, drawn from everyday life. In 2001, *A Child Called It* (Pelzer, 2001) was published, retelling the horrific story of the author's abuse at the hands of his mother during his childhood. It differed from *Chicken Soup for the Soul* in relating just one life story and became a best seller, spawning other books with a similar theme. Both these genres illustrate the four reasons outlined by Roche and Sadowsky (2003) as to why stories are so powerful.

This book is divided into childbirth narratives according to the setting in which the birth occurred and from the perspectives of various witnesses. Sometimes the stories are told through interview or recorded dialogue because this was the chosen vehicle by the contributors. As editors, we have rarely intervened to alter any text because we believe that the integrity of the tales resides in the chosen words of the tellers.

References

Callister L (2004) Making Meaning: Women's Birth Narratives. *Journal of Obstetric, Gynaecology and Neonatal Nursing* **33**: 508–18

Canfield J, Hansen M (1993) *Chicken Soup for the Soul*. New York: HCI

Kirkham M (1997) Stories and childbirth. In M Kirkham, E Perkins (eds.) *Reflections on Midwifery*. London: Bailliere Tindall

Pelzer D (2001) *A Child Called It: One Child's Courage to Survive*. New York: HCI

Roche L, Sadowsky J (2003) The Power of stories: a discussion of why stories are powerful. *International Journal of Information Technology and Management* **2**(4):377–88

CHAPTER 2

Tales from home

Melissa's story

These days our renovated Queenslander worker's cottage in Brisbane's inner city is filled with life – gorgeous, loud Lily who is almost four, beautiful seven-month-old Mia and the duck, two chickens, bush turkeys, pigeons and possums.

I spent much of my twenties finding and achieving my life's purpose (or so I thought). I worked on independent documentaries and reality TV series as a production manager/producer. I was wrangling with crews, coordinating schedules, travelling to conferences and spending lots of time on the computer and phone. I realise now it was the perfect training ground for family life and campaigning for birth reform!

Newly married to my husband Paul, with my biological clock chiming loudly, I researched our pregnancy care and birth options. I decided I wanted maternity care with a known midwife – safe and nurturing. Despite having a dear friend who birthed at home, triumphantly and joyously with a known midwife, I wasn't ready to fully believe in the power and ability of my own body. I wanted care through a birth centre in a hospital and figured this would be the 'best of both worlds'.

I received care from two birth centre midwives. I liked and trusted both of them. All of my appointments were at the hospital and lasted about an hour. My pregnancy with Lily was fairly straightforward, marred only by horrendous morning sickness and a scare that I would be transferred out of birth centre care when Lily was breech (she turned at 34 weeks). A high point of my pregnancy was protesting over the lack of women's access to birthing pools outside our State health department – while 37 weeks pregnant, wearing a hideous pair of maternity togs and sitting in a blow up pool.

During Lily's birth I was cared for at the birth centre by one of my midwives, with my husband and Mum supporting me. I laboured in various active positions and in water. Despite Lily and I coping well, 21 hours after my first contraction at home I was transferred out of the birth centre to the birth suites for a ventouse (vacuum) delivery because I had been actively pushing for more than one hour. Lily was born mostly due to my efforts (pushing on my back) with only a gentle tug on the ventouse. At the time, and for many months afterwards, I felt like the intervention had been necessary and that we had been part of the decision making process.

However, as I learned more about normal birth, I felt that this hospital policy of setting an arbitrary time limit on the second stage seemed to be based on a lack of understanding about the breadth of normality, without thought of consequence about how birth does matter. I had feelings of anger and resentment, and that my body had been cheated out of birthing Lily normally. During my second pregnancy I confronted and worked through these feelings by attending a Healing from Birth support group run by Birthtalk, a birth support and education organisation based in Brisbane, run by a registered midwife, a childbirth educator and mums.

As we were trying to conceive our second child, I knew that during this next birth I wanted to be in an environment where my body could just do what it was meant to do, where my natural hormonal cascade could happen unimpeded by fear or concern about hospital policies. This time I wanted to birth at home.

We were blessed to gain the services of a wonderful midwife in private practice and we started care with her at eight weeks. My husband and I felt supported by her knowledge of 'normal' pregnancy and birth and were glad to have her ability to recognise anything outside of this.

Although most of my anger and disappointment about Lily's birth was directed at the 'system', during my second pregnancy I had to work hard to gain a sense of trust in my body's ability to birth. The most empowering thing was my midwife's strong trust in women's bodies and her lived experience of having seen this so many times.

I also explored my fears and celebrated my body through Georgina Kelly's wonderful course 'The Art of Mindful Birthing'. My birthing 'tigers' reared their heads many times late in my pregnancy. Each time this happened I would read an article Georgina had written in *Natural Parenting* magazine about saying 'yes' to the pain and challenges of labour and birth.

About a week past my estimated due date, my usual evening Braxton Hicks continued throughout the night. At 4am I got up and pottered about. Three weeks before I had had a blessingway, an alternative ceremony to the traditional baby shower which honours a woman's upcoming birthing and mothering journey. My dear friends drew beautiful pictures of their wishes for me during labour. I put these around the walls of my birth space next to the kitchen.

At 6am I lay down on the couch and the contractions spaced out to about every 15 minutes. I rang my midwife at 7am to let her know what was happening. I dozed and called her back later. She and her 11-month-old daughter arrived at 11am while I was reading a story to Lily on the couch, concentrating and breathing deeply through each contraction.

During this time, Paul had stayed home from work and was setting up the birth pool.

By 12.30pm contractions were still about 10 minutes apart. My midwife gave me a wonderful, releasing sacral massage. My contractions became stronger, longer and closer together, every seven minutes. I had a good cry, realising that things were picking up and that there was no going back. My Mum arrived at this time to look after Lily. They played in different parts of the house, checking in on us occasionally.

Ever the family chef, Paul made everyone pasta for lunch. During each contraction I held onto his back, breathing deeply and slowly as he boiled pasta and tore basil, while my midwife gave me Reiki on my sacrum. At 1pm I quickly ate a bowl of pasta and instinctively moved into a restful position on my right side on the birth mat next to the pool in the kitchen. (This is the position I lay in at the birth centre at the end of my labour with Lily while waiting for my obstetrician to arrive at the hospital for the ventouse. I think that the rest allowed Lily to come down the birth canal and is why the ventouse was so gentle when she was born.)

On my side, I began the heavy part of my labour. Within 20 minutes my contractions were coming every three minutes and lasting 70 seconds. However I felt like I had some incredible mind power to be able to shorten my contractions if they were 'too much'. Got to love those birthing hormones!

Our second birth support person and my friend Deirdre, who was to take photos, arrived at 1.30pm. By this stage I really needed verbal and physical reassurance to be able to cope. My midwife massaged my back/sacrum between contractions and held my sacral area during contractions. Our birth support person held my hands and soothed me with gentle words of encouragement. I had a little vomit and registered that I was in transition.

Just after 2pm I said, 'It feels different'. They asked how and I said it felt 'a bit pushy'. I loved that I was able to notice and name this experience in my own time, instead of being 'told'. Shortly after this my waters broke. My midwife was supporting me, talking softly to me between surges, telling me how beautifully I was doing and how well my body was working.

At this stage my midwife checked that I was fully dilated (during my first labour my body had involuntarily begun pushing before I was fully dilated). While doing the vaginal examination she felt my body move my baby back up, instead of down. She felt some tension in my 'Minnie mouse ears' muscles that form part of the pelvic floor (coined as such in The Pink Kit, a childbirth preparation resource which teaches women body awareness for birth, and which I had completed during my pregnancy). She was able to touch me exactly where I needed to relax. I did so, trusting that whatever she suggested would hasten my baby's birth. Sure enough, after I relaxed this area my midwife felt the baby come down. (I wondered if maybe this same muscle tension happened during my labour with Lily.)

Around 2.30pm I realised that the birth was close and that if I wanted this baby to be born in water I had to get into the pool. I tried labouring in a reclining position, holding onto the hand rests in the pool. It didn't feel like it was helping the baby move down, so I changed to a kneeling position, resting over the side of the pool. Paul held my hands and said, 'You're doing great'. I was sipping water occasionally with some Bach flower essences that my midwife gave me to support my process. I was vocalising loudly and deeply with each surge (so much for worrying about our neighbours).

By three o'clock, I could reach down and feel my baby's head. Despite lots of preparation during pregnancy (art/journaling work, using the Epi-no inflatable pelvic floor training device, completing the Pink Kit, etc.), I was still quite challenged by the opening required by my body to push my baby out. However, I was beautifully supported by my midwife, birth support person and Paul. They were able to provide gentle encouragement and explain exactly what was happening.

My midwife said, 'Just let your body do it... so close now.'

I held Paul's hands, strongly pulling them apart as I imagined my pelvis opening up.

My Mum, Lily and my midwife's daughter came in now to watch the birth. My perineum started to stretch as the baby's head was born. It stayed crowning on the widest part after the contraction. I looked wildly into my birth support person's eyes. My eyes locked onto hers, I dug deep for strength I didn't know I had and I said, 'Yes! Yes!' Her eyes filled with tears, as mine do every time I remember that shared moment. With the next contraction the baby's head was out and I heard Lily say behind me, 'There's the baby!'. What wonderful words to hear.

Another contraction at 3.10pm and Mia's body was born, all eight pounds and three ounces of her. My midwife pushed her through the water between my legs and said, 'Reach down and pick up your baby, Melissa'. I looked down, scooped my baby up against my chest and sat back against the opposite side of the pool. Just as I had wished, I had birthed my baby. I looked up at Deirdre taking photos and said, 'I did it! I did it!' At the time I felt like I was yelling these words but I've watched the video and my voice sounds quiet but triumphant.

I said to Lily, 'You've got a sister. You're a big sister now!'

She said, 'A big sister! But Mum, I'm still little!'

I began to have contractions to birth the placenta and Lily asked if I was going to have another baby. I delivered the placenta on a stool 35 minutes after the birth. Mia and I were soon tucked up in bed having our first feed.

We honoured Mia's placenta with a lotus birth. I had a small first degree tear on my perineum and a small labial tear. I chose not to be stitched and on my midwife's advice rested in bed for a week, getting to know my new babe. I was very grateful for this quiet, precious time.

Our postnatal support was amazing, with several visits from our carers, answering a myriad of our questions about breastfeeding, elimination, communication, sleep and our older daughter's processes of accepting her new sibling. We were also greatly blessed to receive nourishing meals and play dates for Lily from my kind friends in the birth community.

I feel like I now truly understand the 'secret' for me to better birthing – being in my own environment and with a midwife with whom I have an intimate, trusting relationship, allowing my body to do what it is made to do.

My experience of the importance of an empowered, joyous birth continues to drive me to improve our maternity care system through my positions as a Maternity Coalition consumer representative on hospital and Government committees. Its hard juggling this work with a young family and often the balance gets out of whack. However, I feel passionately that we need a revolution in birth. In Australia we need our Governments to dismantle the barriers to homebirth practice, including an unsupportive regulatory system and lack of visiting rights, prescribing rights or insurance. The culture of fear among caregivers and health bureaucrats needs to be confronted. These are barriers to good midwifery care in any setting. To expand access to homebirth, we need to fix the whole system.

Esme's story

Esme was referred to the caseload team when she was 34 weeks into her second pregnancy. She had attended a consultant antenatal clinic and become very upset and voiced her fears about her ability to give birth to the midwife she saw. I telephoned Esme and explained about how the caseload team worked (one-to-one care from a named midwife throughout pregnancy, and on-call for labour and birth) and offered her an initial visit to discuss her needs and help her consider what she really wanted for the birth of her baby.

I visited Esme and her husband at home and for most of the first visit just listened to Esme explaining what had happened in her first labour and how that had made her feel. She was very tearful and anxious throughout this time and I could tell that her first experience had made a deep and lasting impression on her, one that she wasn't sure she could overcome. Esme had lost all faith in her ability to birth her baby without help, despite her first birth being, on paper at least, a textbook, straightforward, fairly quick process. Esme had felt so frightened by this experience and its effect on her bonding with her first child that she needed something different to happen this time.

I felt I needed to put Esme right at the centre of her care, but more importantly, make her *feel* she was at the centre of her care, to give her back her power and her ability to make choices that would be respected. Esme was considering asking for an elective caesarean section, as this was one way of her regaining control. I offered another suggestion – homebirth. Homebirth is an incredibly simple way of putting the woman back in charge. She controls access to the birth, simply by being in her own home. Also, by being in her own surroundings a woman is more likely to be able to relax and allow her body to labour without added stress. Esme and Phil were both interested in this idea and I recommended a couple of websites for them to visit for more information and also some real stories from homebirthing parents. I also mentioned waterbirth as an option. Women who have laboured and birthed their babies in water have commented to me about how safe they felt in their pools as 'no-one could get at me without my co-operation'. One woman told me that the pool 'provided me with a safe nest in which to lie my baby'.

Our first meeting was an important foundation for the relationship that was to develop between Esme, Phil and me. I arranged to meet Esme (and Phil when he wasn't at work) each week for the remainder of her pregnancy as I recognised how important this relationship building was, especially for Esme, who had felt let down and ignored by previous caregivers. I also gave Esme and Phil some birth stories written by women who had had a first traumatic experience and then a second empowering birth. Sharing stories in this way makes it all seem more real and possible.

Throughout the remaining weeks we carried on learning about each other. Esme and Phil decided that a homebirth was what they wanted (and needed) and that they were also going to get a pool, although Esme was unsure if she wanted to actually give birth in it. Esme continued to voice concerns, doubts and fears, often becoming tearful and scared. I asked if she had ever considered seeing a homeopath and gave her the contact details for someone who had recently talked to our caseload group.

Esme did go to the homeopath regularly throughout the rest of her pregnancy, using the suggested remedies which she felt helped her sleep and feel more positive. She also invested in a homeopathic birth kit to use during labour.

Obstetrically Esme's pregnancy continued uneventfully to her due date and beyond. Induction of labour was not what she wanted, so as we approached 42 weeks we discussed what to do next. Esme felt she wanted to take each day at a time and I supported her in this decision. As it happened, labour started on the day Esme reached 42 weeks, so we never had to put our plans for monitoring or liquor volume scans into practice.

At 2am I received a text message from Esme saying she thought labour was starting and that she had been having pains since 10pm the previous night. I replied, offering a visit if needed, but Esme felt she was all right for the time being. I encouraged her to rest, eat and drink as needed, and have a soak in the bath if she felt that would help.

She rang back at about 4.15am to say contractions were strong, every 10 minutes. Her voice sounded panicky, although she was using her TENS machine. Phil was filling the pool. I got dressed and set off. When I arrived Esme was obviously feeling very distressed; she had the TENS set to a high level. She was frightened, contracting strongly and regularly, and she didn't know what to do. We discussed the options – wait and see, an internal examination, or go to hospital. Esme chose to be examined, but when I told her that her cervix was 4cm dilated, she panicked further, saying she couldn't possibly cope without an epidural and that she wanted to go to hospital. We talked for a while longer and I suggested that she at least try the pool (which was full by this time, and lovely and warm and inviting) before going to hospital. Esme was quite adamant that we needed to go to hospital, so I left her in the bedroom and had a quiet word with Phil, hoping he could encourage her to try the pool. It worked. Esme finally said she'd give it a go. She was scared to take off her TENS machine and get in the pool as she thought the pain might be unbearable. I set up the entonox so Esme could start using it straight away and reassured and encouraged her. She got into the pool and the change in her was immediate; she relaxed and smiled, and allowed her body to get on with its job. She didn't even ask about the entonox.

Esme's labour was longer than her first labour, but began at the speed that she could deal with mentally, one step at a time. There were times when she became tearful and upset, and we encouraged and supported her, with Phil giving homeopathic remedies and tea and toast as necessary. Throughout labour, the baby's heart observations were reassuring and all Esme's observations were normal. About an hour and a half before the baby's birth Esme started using entonox to help with her contractions, but, after getting in the pool, she never once requested to go to hospital, have an epidural or a caesarean section.

Esme pushed spontaneously and physiologically throughout her expulsive phase. I did have to ask her to stand up after the birth of the head as there was no sign of restitution or further progress. Esme put her foot on the side of the pool and the baby slipped out easily and I passed her quickly to her ecstatic mum who was saying, 'Look, look, our baby, I did it, I did it!'

After a while Esme got out of the pool and cuddled up on the sofa with her new baby. The cord was clamped and then cut by Phil and the placenta delivered physiologically.

Later on I helped Esme into the shower and then snuggled her up in bed with her new daughter – Phil was still doing the tea and toast and the couple were talking excitedly about introducing their son to his new sister.

During our postnatal visits I could see how proud of herself Esme was. A week later she said, 'I have to keep saying to myself she was born here, just over there, it just makes me smile.' Phil and Ethan were happily splashing in the birthpool which had now taken up home in the garden.

This is midwifery, putting women in the centre, helping them realise their potential. No matter what their level of 'risk' women need to be encouraged to be included in decisions about their care, to make them realise their part in the whole, miraculous process.

Alissa's story

A homebirth wasn't our own idea. It started with an offer from Denis Walsh. Neil (my husband) and I had met Denis through our church. He and his wife used to be our home-group leaders. We happened to meet Denis soon after we decided to try for a baby, and when we told him our plans he said, 'If you conceive, I'll do a homebirth for you, with a birthing pool.' We knew Denis was experienced and had a good reputation, and I liked the idea of having a midwife I knew.

When we did conceive, soon afterwards, I wasn't entirely sure about a homebirth and decided to find out more. Another midwife friend, Pam, told me that in Holland 30% to 40% of births were homebirths and the outcomes were just as good as those in Britain. Statistically, homebirths were as safe as hospital births, provided the pregnancy was straightforward and there were no special risk factors. She said she preferred doing homebirths because the women were more relaxed, which meant that labour hurt less and went more smoothly. They needed less pain relief and the baby was less likely to become distressed, so the 'cascade of intervention' was less likely to begin. She also said that Denis was very experienced and would know in good time if anything was going wrong, so that I could get to hospital quickly – and we lived only five minutes' drive from Leicester General. She lent me a book by Sheila Kitzinger on homebirth, with stories and photos of happy experiences. Between Pam and Sheila, I was convinced. A doctor I trusted, Sarah, also approved. She also said women were more relaxed at home, so labour hurt less and went more smoothly, and added that you avoided the risk of cross-infection. She thought that the main risk was of haemorrhaging, and recommended that the midwives should have some blood plasma to put up as a drip to maintain blood volume until I got to hospital as a precaution. Denis said that was OK, so we decided to go ahead.

Neil was a bit doubtful initially, but agreed on hearing Pam and Sarah's opinions. Unlike some people, we had no complicating factors to mention, even though I was 38 at the time of birth. Our GP just said it was up to us, but his practice didn't attend homebirths because of lack of expertise. But we didn't need them to, anyway. We also read up on waterbirth and decided to hire a pool.

Denis roped in a colleague, Mark, and a student midwife. They did all my antenatal care at home (no queuing!) and I liked them all. I discovered that if I did have to go into hospital at least one of them would stay with me all the time. Normally, in hospital, midwives would come and go (at that time, anyway) as the shifts changed.

Four days before my due date, my waters broke at 2am and contractions began. I'd expected the baby to come late (like my relatives' babies), and we'd just had the house repainted, so the living room was full of stuff from other rooms and there wasn't enough space to set up the pool. Neil spent the rest of the night shifting everything, while I had a snack (tinned peaches), then wandered about wearing a TENS machine and answering questions about where things went.

Denis came out soon after 2am, checked me and said he'd come back at 8 o'clock to see how things were going, then probably go away again and come back once labour was established. Once the living-room was clear, I tried to have a shower, but couldn't as I had to be sick, and then the contractions seemed to be getting close enough together to make showering difficult. By the time Denis came back they were less than five minutes apart and quite strong. He examined me and said I was over 4cm dilated and he would stay on. He rang his colleagues to ask them to come. Neil started setting up the pool and when Mark arrived he joined in. By this time I was quite strongly focused inwards and was only dimly aware of their voices talking about nuts and how the connector wouldn't fit on the kitchen tap. (We hadn't had a trial run as we should have done.) Denis gave me some gas and air and I just concentrated on using that and on doing breathing exercises, which I liked. The contracting sensations were strong but not painful. It felt like my body had just taken over and was getting on with things with no help needed from the mind. Most of this time I spent on all fours, which felt just right. Earlier on I'd tried several upright positions including leaning on Neil. My body seemed to know what it wanted. I was near the glass doors to the back garden, and Neil told me afterwards that a cat had walked over the lawn and stopped and watched me with interest for some time! I didn't notice it, but I did notice the beautiful sunny weather and birdsong drifting in from Evington Park, just behind our garden. It was May bank holiday.

By about 10am the pool was full and the water heating up. (It was large, over 5 feet long and oval, and came with a small heater.) I vaguely heard comments about it taking a long time to get warm, but nothing really registered with me – I just wanted to get on with things. Neil came and read me some passages from the Bible. I'd written a list beforehand of ones I would like to hear. They were the only words that seemed to get through to me and I really liked hearing them. They reassured and uplifted me. He also put a tape of songs on: psalms set to music, by Ian White. I loved those too.

Denis examined me again and said I might be giving birth before the pool was ready. I didn't care – I just wanted to concentrate. I tried a couple of other positions: I remember supported squatting, with Neil on one side and Mark on the other. Mark said it brought back happy memories, not of his own children being born (he has five), but of rugby scrums he'd been in!

I was in second stage by about 11am, and the pool was finally heated up by noon. When Denis eventually got my attention and told me I could get in, I didn't want to move – I was busy, I felt. After some persuasion I did waddle over and climb in, and it felt lovely. It was great to be supported by the warm water, and I seemed to relax more between contractions. There was no actual pain, but when the baby's head crowned it did burn and feel uncomfortable – especially as it seemed to stay where it was, just going up and down a bit, for a long time. I asked Denis if he could do anything but he said, 'Nothing physical'.

I'm not sure what non-physical things he might have meant, but I just carried on. I guess he knew I was all right and the baby was all right. He'd been monitoring its heartbeat with a special waterproof Sonicaid. After a two and a half hour second stage, Denis asked me to go on all fours. He helped the shoulders out, then scooped the baby out of the water. David was born at 1.22pm, about 11 hours after labour began. Apparently he was a bit slow to breathe (which was quite common with water babies), so they played oxygen on his face and then did something else – 1 couldn't see what, it was all going on behind me, but then David started breathing. We later found out there had been a problem with the oxygen cylinder. It hadn't started working straight away. Happily for us we weren't aware of it at the time. The midwives cut the cord, wrapped him up and gave him to Neil to hold.

They asked me to get out of the birthing pool to deliver the placenta. I was very tired by then and climbing out felt like one of the hardest things I'd ever done. I had an injection and delivered the placenta, then sat on the sofa (which was covered in a sheet of plastic), and held David. He looked at me with blue eyes. I was so pleased and relieved he was OK. I had been concerned about my above-average risk of Down's syndrome, at the age of 38, and we hadn't had any tests. But he was perfect, and a good size too (eight pounds and one ounce). Going upstairs to have a wash felt like climbing a mountain. But once I'd had one, with the help of the student midwife, how wonderful it was to be in the double bed, with Neil on the other side and the baby in between us. We gazed at him in wonder – was he really ours? I felt euphoric and Neil did too. After telling each other several dozen times how sweet the baby was, we rang up everyone we could think of to share the news. Neil didn't have to leave, and I didn't have to eat hospital food. We were so happy and excited. We learnt about nappies, soothing and bathing together. Even the first nappy change was exciting, because we had our first-ever baby.

I did have some problems breast-feeding and David had virtually no food for three days. Happily, Pam then arrived back from holiday and sorted that out. Thanks to her, David had a year's breast milk he wouldn't otherwise have had.

I think that being there from the start helped Neil to bond with the baby. He has always been a very hands-on dad and is still devoted to both our sons. We had another boy five years later, also delivered at home by Denis. This time I sat and cuddled the baby in the pool. I saw his skin change from blue to pink as he took his first breath. It was magical.

Three days after David's birth, I remember looking into his eyes and feeling a huge surge of love. I knew I would do anything for him. I would give him the very best I could for the rest of his life.

Looking back, I think Pam was right: I did feel more relaxed at home than I would have in hospital. It also helped having three midwives that I already knew and liked. I didn't have to worry about how I was getting on with them, or about what was going on round me: I could just focus on my body.

It was one of the happiest days of my life, and will always be a wonderful memory.

CHAPTER 3

Tales from hospital

Fia's interview with a midwife

This interview is about the occurrences that prevent midwives from maintaining normal childbirth practices in a Swedish conventional maternity unit.

Exemplary midwifery practice has been described by midwives and women as supporting the normalcy of pregnancy and birth, applying vigilance and attention to detail, respecting the uniqueness of the woman and creating a setting that is respectful and reflects the woman's needs. This has been summarised as 'the art of doing nothing well', and is in accordance with a definition of normal childbirth as a physiological process where medical interventions are used only when necessary. It requires that midwives base their practices on scientific knowledge and reliable experience. However, research has indicated a high rate of interventions during labour, both with women at low risk and high risk; such interventions include augmentation, artificial rupture of membranes and episiotomies. Moreover, a study based on a Swedish national sample showed that only 22% of women giving birth were cared for in accordance with evidence-based recommendations. Studies have also shown that there are notable deviations between different maternity units. The reasons why interventions were carried out could often not be understood from partograms or documentation.

Intrapartum midwifery care has been subject to research, and different studies have taken midwives' and women's perspectives. However, questions as to what influences midwives to perform superfluous interventions, causing them to abandon recommendations and general guidelines, have not been asked. It is against this backdrop that this interview was carried out. It is an attempt to discuss, describe and comprehend what prevents midwives in a Swedish conventional maternity unit from maintaining normal childbirth practices. The midwife interviewed has been working in one of the 10 largest delivery units in Sweden for more than 30 years.

The clinic has been the subject of a previous intervention study, attempting to influence intrapartum care to follow the WHO's recommendations for care in normal birth, and the midwife interviewed has been involved in previous discussions on the subject of how to maintain normal birth practices.

The interview took place in a secluded room, and an interview guide comprising one general question: 'Could you tell me about the latest childbirth you assisted?' was used.

Follow-up questions were written on a piece of paper in sight of both the interviewer and the interviewee. The interview took about 70–80 minutes and was taped and then transcribed verbatim.

Midwife: Ok, well, the last childbirth I assisted... I was working an afternoon shift, and the patient was a nullipara. I had met her before, when she had visited the maternity unit a few weeks earlier, she had taken rincinus oil then and suffered from stomach pains and the contractions had started. She was a bit different, so to speak, 21 years old, and I got the impression she had been through quite a lot in her teens. She came from X-burgh, and was seeing a man who had three children previously. Anyway, now she had gone full term, the contractions had started, and she had come in to the maternity unit the previous night. She had been in great pains and had been given an epidural anaesthesia early on in the process. A midwifery student had assisted her before me. When my shift started, the patient was in frenzy...

Interviewer: She had been at the maternity unit since the night before then?

Midwife: That's right, but she had been given that epidural anaesthesia, so she must have slept for a few hours. I suppose she had been stimulated as usual, she had been open about 8cm since 12 o'clock. She did ok, but then, you know, as often happens with epidurals, they don't... she was in pain... the baby was pressing against the pelvic floor and she nearly fainted... well, so we decided on augmentation... That went really well, and out came a beautiful little boy. But the mother was so exhausted she fell asleep (perplexed)... I never experienced that before... Well, anyway, the mother and I had spoken, the previous time she had come in, about the delivery, about what to expect... and, well, I got the impression she was quite scared then. During labour she screamed a lot... and, when I examined her she was really swollen around the edges... so I called for the obstetrician, who gave her a paracervical anaesthesia. To give the woman some breathing space, you know...

Another thing was that she wanted you to be with her, in the delivery room, the whole time. And the father, well he was completely hysterical, so the doctor had to take him outside to explain the situation to him... he thought the woman was about to die... He was so frustrated about the midwifery student who had assisted them before my shift started... he called her a buffoon, said she had not done or said anything... said he had wanted to throw her out...but I felt he had great confidence in me, the father...he appreciated that I was doing things. But the epidural had been given too early of course...

Interviewer: Really? What do you mean too early?

Midwife: Well, I don't think she had progressed far enough in the labour process [laughing] to be given that epidural. According to the criteria we work by, with amnions broken, regular contractions, and that the woman must be open about 3–4 centimetres... well I don't think... I suppose she was experiencing the contractions as really strong, but...

Interviewer: Ok, so she was given that epidural too early, you say...

Midwife: Well, yes. We, the midwives at the unit, spoke about it afterwards, you see... and we thought that maybe she should have been given morphine instead... 'cause the epidural... well, I think it confuses the body... you know, first there are contractions, and then there aren't any... you interrupt the process... But at the same time, she was in pain, and well it's easy to take to the good old epidural... and then it proceeded as it did, with difficulties to stimulate contractions, and painkillers... but I felt good being able to help her get the paracervical anaesthesia.

Interviewer: After this story, I'm keen to ask you how you perceive this birth? In terms of normal or obstructed birth, how would you classify this one?

Midwife: Oh, well, it didn't exactly follow normal procedures...I mean progress stopped, didn't it?

Interviewer: Is that what makes it an obstructed labour, in your opinion? That progress stopped?

Midwife: Well, no...the pain she experienced, I must say it was extraordinary. She was panicking in a way that you don't see very often. Still it's interesting to think that she came into the unit, and contractions had started, and then things got complicated with that epidural...?

But on the other hand, this patient was prepared to accept any kind of intervention... I can compare her to one patient I met during my last nightshift. Her file stated that the pregnancy had been normal and that she didn't want too much pain relief, but that she would consider an epidural if things got difficult. She came in, and was open about 1cm, but as soon as it got a bit more critical, she didn't want it any more, she was quick to demand an epidural. In those cases I believe we could be better at supporting the women, informing them of the normalcy of the situation, encouraging them to dare to continue without an epidural. That it's a matter of working together, that it will hurt, that she will want to die... yeah, well that's what they say!

Interviewer: Do you say that to the women, that they will want to die?

Midwife: Well, no, but sometimes it's what I'd like to say. Most women reach a point in the process where they think they can't push one more time, but it's usually only for a short period of time that its really critical. If we could be there then, and support them, then perhaps... well, it's very few women who come in to the unit filled with positive energy, ready to give birth.

Interviewer: How do they feel, the birthing women, when they come to the maternity unit?

Midwife: They complain about pains...or rather, at the beginning of the process, before active labour sets in, in the latent phase, well then they're pleased... but as soon as it gets a bit more critical, you know, at 5–6cms, they don't want it any more. When it's time to push they complain about being tired, and about pain. 'You must help me, I can't do this any more,' they say. They want you to put an end to it, to augment the labour...or, one doesn't really know what they want, but...

Interviewer: Do they say: 'I want augmentation'?

Midwife: No. They say: 'You must help me, I can't do this any more.' And I ask, 'How can we help you?' And perhaps I suggest augmentation...[laughing] and well they accept, and we proceed with augmentation...or I say: 'Let's try a little while longer', but one has to use a firm tone of voice then, because they are tired and...

Interviewer: You mentioned, just then, that you ask the birthing women what they want you to do for them...?

Midwife: Yes, I don't think they really know... they want it to end...

Interviewer: Well, this is interesting. How do you respond, when the women say they can't do it any more?

Midwife: I find it difficult to know how firm to be with them... I try to tell them that they are young and healthy, that it's all normal... but I find that it is more often the dad who needs to be assured that it's normal, they get really scared, they've never seen their women in this state...

Interviewer: Do you perceive that many men find the birth frightening?

Midwife: Yes, absolutely. They can't for their lives imagine what the woman will act like. I think it would be good if they were better prepared, if they had some knowledge about what the birthing process is about... there are definitely knowledge gaps. They don't know when to come in to the unit, or what constitutes a normal birth.

Interviewer: Do many women come in to the unit too early?

Midwife: Oh yes, but I believe we have become much better at informing women that they are not yet in active labour, that it's too early for them. For the most part they understand... and I think the word has spread as well, that they can't come in too early. But then there are some you feel you just can't send home... and, well, an early epidural is common in those cases. Like one woman who came in a while back... she demanded an epidural, but I thought the contractions weren't strong enough. I would have liked to encourage her to wait a while longer, but I didn't have time to be with her, it was the end of my shift and she wanted that epidural... I know she gave birth later that night, with artificial rupture of the membranes and stimulation...

Interviewer: The interventions you talk about now, would you say that they are part of a normal birth process nowadays?

Midwife: Well, yes... artificial rupture of the membranes, epidurals and oxytocin drip... are definitely part of normal procedure. It is more rare that the patient doesn't receive interventions... 25–30% get an epidural.

Interviewer: Is that always at the patient's request?

Midwife: No, I don't think you could say that. We discuss this subject at work sometimes, I mean who... if it's stress that makes us midwives... I think we intervene too much sometimes, more than necessary. There was one woman, who was really looking forward to giving birth. She paid attention to her body's signals and acted accordingly. I was just a spectator... and then, I said something or suggested something, and the woman replied: 'Where's the fire?' That was an eye-opener. Just standing there, doing nothing. It's so unusual. Otherwise one is so active, in some way or other. This is something one has to learn, to be more of a spectator.

Interviewer: Learn what, do you mean?

Midwife: What I mean is... I have been a midwife for 30 years now... and things have happened during those years, and one kind of just tags along. One doesn't question much. And now... well, now we do artificial ruptures of the membranes... augmentation and so on... to quicken the process...

Interviewer: I wonder if you could elaborate on the subject of 'making it finish', it's a rather common comment in the case notes; 'Gave drip, to make it finish.'

Midwife: Ok, well, it's when you're with the patient... you don't want it to be a lengthy process... not for her either... and then, you want to show that you've done something too. I think that's a big part of it... we discuss this too sometimes, that when you hand over the patient you don't want to feel you haven't done anything for her. It's stressful, and you wonder what she would say... if someone took over and suddenly things started to happen...

Interviewer: Do you recognise that feeling?

Midwife: Yes, to some extent, I do... I have to admit that... But at the same time I think about how a quick delivery is not necessarily a better delivery, that the experience is not necessarily better because it's quick. But that's one of the things that have changed over the years... although now I'm beginning to see a change again, where we are allowing the process to take a bit more time. But it is very individual. At the unit, not too long ago, we compared two cases; one was a woman who declined the offer of augmentation because she was terrified of needlesticks. Even though it probably prolonged the birthing process she was happy, and everything went well. The other case was a woman who had a really quick progress, and still she was still given drip. The second stage lasted no longer than 20 minutes. So, that shows how different the deliveries can be...

Interviewer: So what do you think about the time aspect? It appears to be rather important...

Midwife: Often when parents come into the unit they start by asking how long I think the delivery will take. There are a lot of expectations there... And I try to say that it usually takes time, the literature states that the woman will open about 1cm per hour, and then the second stage... I mean, it takes time.

Interviewer: And do the parents accept that answer?

Midwife: Many are impatient. Especially those who come into the unit before active labour has set in. Their experience is that it's taking too long, and they get fixated on the time aspect. But if you think about it it's seldom a question of 24 hours of actual labour.

Interviewer: As I understand it the time aspect is crucial. Both for the patient and the midwife.

Midwife: We have discussed this too, especially in relation to epidurals and sleeping... If the woman is in active labour when the epidural is given, how long should she then be asleep for, before we start stimulating her, before she is given oxytocin augmentation?

Interviewer: Is that what you discuss – giving augmentation?

Midwife: Yes, and artificial rupture.

Interviewer: What about getting up, walking around...?

Midwife: No, the discussions are centred on artificial rupture and oxytocin augmentation.

Interviewer: You want to do something?

Midwife: That appears to be the case, yes [laughing].

Interviewer: You have mentioned epidurals and stimulation several times during our talk...

Midwife: Yes, it's not often you give an epidural and then no stimulation to get it started again. But then, I suppose, we haven't really tried just waiting to see what happens.

Interviewer: What are the guidelines for starting stimulation?

Midwife: Lack of progression... but the time span between when the epidural is given and when you start stimulating differs a lot. If the woman is given the epidural in the night, say at one o'clock, you might not start the stimulation until the morning shift arrives. But at other times the midwife might examine the woman after just a few hours, and if there has been no progression since the epidural was given, she might start stimulation.

Interviewer: And there are no guidelines for that?

Midwife: No, there are no general guidelines... and that's also something we've discussed. Perhaps we should have some regulations around this, like they have in other places. Here it's up to each midwife to decide... I think we should set up guidelines.

Interviewer: I'd like to return to the story about the couple you last assisted. Which interventions were carried out during that delivery?

Midwife: Well, she was given pain relief, and she had an epidural. That's what she asked for. When she started to feel pain again, that's exactly when we changed shifts and I took over, she was given the paracervical ...

Interviewer: And do you believe that other midwives would have handled it the same way? You said the situation was a bit panicked...

Midwife: Well, yes, but then you wonder if she shouldn't have been given that paracervical... earlier, because the father was really upset. The obstetrician noticed that too, and took him outside, to explain that everything was normal. That calmed him down...

Interviewer: Well that's interesting. The obstetrician takes the father aside to tell him that everything is normal, after all those interventions...?

Midwife: Yes, but that was because I hadn't had any time to focus on the dad. I saw that the obstetrician took the father outside, and it was only afterwards that he told me he felt he had had to tell the father it was all normal, to calm him down...I don't know [laughing]...

Interviewer: Normalcy of pregnancy...

Midwife: Yeah, right...

Interviewer: Can we talk a little bit about what information you get from the records... it states what kind of pain relief and so on the woman wishes to get... is it also stated how she feels about emotional support? Is that something you discuss?

Midwife: No, I wouldn't say so, no. You ask about how they want the birthing process to be, of course, but not that specifically, no. But most women expect you to examine them often, even if we try not to examine them too often, at least not in the early stages. Later on, when they start to push we might examine them a bit more often...

Interviewer: When you say push, is it the women who want to push or...?

Midwife: Yes, it's not often you have to command them to push. If anything, it's the other way around, that you try to tell them not to push, if it's too early in the birthing process...

Interviewer: That's interesting too, I think. I mean, it's not really established what makes you push and why... Anyway, would you say that you examine the woman because she wants you to?

Midwife: No because I want to know [laughing]... know that the process is normal.

Interviewer: So what is a normal process?

Midwife: Progression, that she is opening up... if she doesn't, we do artificial rupture of the membranes.

Interviewer: Do you always perform artificial rupture of the membranes first?

Midwife: No, it depends... sometimes you start with the membranes, so that maybe you don't have to give syntocinon... I remember one birth where everything proceeded perfectly, and the baby was born in its membranes, that was amazing!

Interviewer: But if everything hadn't proceeded perfectly...?

Midwife: Well there is always a dialogue... I imagine... you tell them that there hasn't been any progression and that maybe they want to get up and walk...

Interviewer: But there is always a dialogue?

Midwife: I try, I try. But of course, it isn't always that...

Interviewer: But would you say a dialogue precedes all interventions carried out?

Midwife: Not always... I always explain why I do one thing or another, but no, a dialogue does not always precede the decision... it's very seldom the women don't want the intervention...

Interviewer: But when they first come in to the maternity unit, what are their expectations?

Midwife: Well the records often state that the pregnancy has been normal, that the woman is looking forward to giving birth. That she'd like to try bathing, would like pain relief, might want an epidural... wants to breast feed... well that's about it... so we often give them epidurals...

Interviewer: Do you believe that we could change this? Do we even want to influence the women in a different direction?

Midwife: Right, do we? I don't know. Trends come and go... in the eighties we hardly gave any pain relief at all, but now there is a lot of it... it will change again.

Interviewer: Do you think the changes are a result of patients' requests?

Midwife: It is always hard to say anything about ongoing processes. But I wonder if it could be the patients' requests, I mean they don't have the knowledge...

Interviewer: Yes, one wonders about cardiotocography and epidurals for example, could it really be the patients demanding this?

Midwife: Well, I think about the right to pain relief, the law that was passed in 1971. That must have been a demand coming from patients... but I don't know how we ended up here... people are scared, there are a lot of caesareans... I think what we need to do is refocus on prenatal information. I mean, it's like bicycling, you can't do it without training.

But I think it's coming back again. All these interventions, with epidurals and stimulations, and the stopping of contractions and the restarting them... I don't know why it's like this now... but sometimes I find myself thinking: 'Are women not capable of giving birth normally any more?'

Cas's story

Flashback: Voices swirl. I can hear my own breathing. It's as if I'm inside my body somewhere, hiding, listening. My eyes open and I feel the weight of heavy plastic on my face. I feel bound. Wires everywhere.

'What's going on?' I try to say, but can't because of the oxygen mask on my face. I struggle to remove it. Somebody tries to shove it back on. I tear it off anyway.

'Where's my baby?' I spit out. 'Where's my baby?'

It was a fairly typical scenario: private obstetrician recommends an early induction because of borderline pre-eclampsia symptoms. Induction ends up failing and I get rushed to theatre for an emergency caesarean.

I remember feeling completely helpless when the catatonic contractions began. I wanted to use the loo but felt like nothing would come out. I got more and more upset and frustrated. My husband sat there not knowing what to do. I felt useless, like everyone around me was waiting for me to fail.

By the time the operation was ordered, I had resigned myself to the reality of being sliced open. I felt like I had given it a shot but that somehow my body had let me down. No one had prepared me for what was to follow.

During the operation, I felt a sudden sharp pain in my pelvis. I anxiously turned my head to the anaesthetist and said, 'I can feel that! I can feel pain.'

He patted my shoulder and said, 'It's just a bit of tugging.'

A moment later, another burst of sharp pain and I cried out, 'I felt that! Please, I felt pain!'

The obstetrician looked up and said, 'Can you feel that?'

More pain. 'Yes!' I cried.

'I'm pressing on your pelvis,' she said nonchalantly. Then she immediately put her head down and hurried to get baby Liam out of me while I cried in pain. They took him out and whisked him away before I could even get a good look at him. I didn't care about the pain at that stage. I just wanted my baby. But once they'd taken him out, they gave me a general anaesthetic. The next thing I knew, I woke up with that damn mask on my face.

They brought Liam to me in recovery (after much insistence) and I held my baby for the first time. Wayne had taken photos of him in the crib for me to look at later. He was petite and round and I loved him instantly. I asked to put him to breast and he had his first suckle. He seemed to know what to do and I felt relieved.

Suddenly though, I felt anxious and unable to breathe. The anaesthetist and obstetrician ordered an electrocardiogram, just in case there was anything wrong with my heart.

'My heart?' I thought, 'What have they done to me?'

Later that night I went to sleep with Liam tucked under my arm. I was just glad it was all over and that I could get on with admiring this little being they had brought me and told me was mine.

Within a couple of days, the aftershocks struck. A friend came by and changed his nappy. I just let her take over but something inside of me wanted to say, 'He's mine, I think. Maybe I should be doing that.' But I couldn't say it because, at that point, I felt like I had to ask everyone's permission to do anything for him.

The day after Liam was born, the obstetrician walked in, patted me on the leg and said, 'Not going to have a big family then, are we?' I was devastated.

Childhood memories of tearing about the house with my three siblings were something I wanted for my own brood and I definitely wanted a brood, at least four! I suddenly felt robbed of that. It was as if she was saying birth was no good for me and that I should quit while I was ahead. Later on, I reflected on how much damage those words had caused and how I had to reclaim my heartfelt desire to have more children and to birth them as well.

Within a couple of weeks of Liam's birth, Wayne and I made the decision to pack up and head for the UK for a couple of years. That was fine by me. I wanted to get as far away from everything as possible. I felt ashamed and like I had no mothering instincts. I dared not tell anyone else how I felt lest they take Liam away from me. I was scared and alone and wanted to be somewhere else. So, somewhere else we went.

We settled in Windsor, south west of London. There were lots of parks and lovely surroundings, plus a castle just up the road but I didn't know anyone, nor did I know how to meet anyone. After about a month, the local health visitor came by and told me about a local group that ran at a nearby church each week. I relished the opportunity to meet other mums but, at the same time, was enjoying my isolation. It was as if I wanted to hide what was really going on – the nightmares, flashbacks and panic that had set in. I didn't want anyone to think I was depressed or wasn't managing, but the truth has a way of declaring itself. After a couple of months I felt paralysed by panic. I'd stand at the kitchen window motionless while flashbacks of the surgery replayed in my head. I'd be terrified to walk out the front door lest I ran into someone I knew or saw a pregnant woman. I didn't want anything to do with pregnant women. I was never having another baby and didn't want to be reminded of the fact.

One day, a midwife at the clinic asked me if I'd take their postnatal depression survey. She said that I should see my GP about a referral to a counsellor and a support group. I didn't want to go to a support group though. What I was experiencing seemed removed from depression and I didn't want to sit around listening to how sad everyone was. I opted for counselling and, because they suspected I was a suicide risk, the midwife came and visited every week for eight weeks.

She probably saved my life because at that point, I felt so worthless and hopeless, unworthy of my gorgeous child and long-suffering husband that I wanted to die. I wanted the flashbacks and nightmares to be over with.

When Liam was nearly two, we moved back to Australia and I felt obliged to have another baby, even though, inside, I really didn't want to be pregnant again. Every bone in my body was screaming, 'You're not ready yet!'

As my pregnancy unfolded, I started to deal with the fallout from Liam's birth. I went from being scared and overwrought at the prospect of having another baby to feeling empowered and confident. Alas, my second baby's birth was a repeat caesarean. His birth hadn't unfolded how I had hoped, but it was, nevertheless, an empowering experience where I felt respected.

Just 10 months after Daniel was born I found out I was pregnant once again, so whether I liked it or not, I had to deal with the issues that were still plaguing me. The stats were not in my favour: I was short, a tad plump, had a small delivery to pregnancy interval, a history of complications in previous births and had never ever actively laboured. However, I had read medical journal articles and books on the subject and decided, on balance, it was safer to go for a natural birth than a third caesarean section.

I knew that I had to give it my all to have a vaginal birth, and not just a vaginal birth – a natural, ecstatic birth. I wanted to go for the fences if only to prove to myself that birth could be a good and safe experience without surgery.

So I set about creating the environment I needed to optimise my chances of a natural birth. I decided that support for a vaginal birth after two caesareans would be hard to come by where I lived, so I booked in to a maternity hospital with a good vaginal birth after caesarean section rate, two hours from my home. I knew a midwife in Nambour and we arranged a deal with the local obstetrician for a shared care arrangement. I would see my midwife antenatally and she would attend the birth. The visits with my midwife were lovely. We'd spend an hour or so talking and working through issues at each session. I envisaged myself as an athlete training for championship event. I also kept a list of my needs and fears. Each session we would go through the list. Some items were hard to write down and share but I held to the philosophy that one more thing shared prior to birth was one less thing to hold me up in labour. I didn't have any scans as I felt the need to go within and connect with my baby on a more primal, intuitive level.

My due date came and went, as I knew it would, and a couple of weeks went by. By the end of the third week I was well and truly over being pregnant. I asked my midwife if she'd do a stretch and sweep. She couldn't reach too far in with her tiny fingers but within a day I started to lose my mucous plug so I figured something was happening. I had acupuncture on the Monday and on the Tuesday we headed up to Nambour for another antenatal appointment. We decided to stay up there for a few days at a nearby hotel. That night, labour began. After the third rush to the toilet, I figured that this was what contractions felt like. In the morning they were bitey and closer together. I phoned my friend, Jodie, to come, but by the time she arrived, the regular contractions had dissipated. I felt deflated and embarrassed. Had I been wrong? It went on like this for nearly two days. In the end, I felt like I had to get away from everyone, so I booked into the maternity unit and sent Wayne back to Brisbane with the kids to find a babysitter. Shortly after they left, my waters started leaking. Progress, at last! Midwife Vicki came in while I was chatting to a woman in the opposite room and watched me through one contraction. She promptly told me to go back to my room for some quiet time. Being a talker, this was easier said than done but having some quiet time alone was exactly what I needed. I had midwife Lynne run me a bath in the birth suite and I just relaxed for a couple of hours. Wayne was on his way back and Jodie not far behind.

Late that night, I felt like I'd lost the plot. Jodie gave me a massage and Wayne disappeared to get some sleep. It was going to be a long night. I sat on the toilet for ages with midwife Vicki by my side. I was having bladder trouble and it brought back memories from my 'labour' with Liam. After a while, Vicki announced that my contractions were 3 minutes apart. I was euphoric. It was real now.

We moved to the shower where finally, my bladder gave way and the midwives poured ice cold water over my head while the steaming jetstream belted into my lower back. The contractions were coming thick and fast now. I moved to the bath and immediately felt cooler and more serene. Midwife Lynne sat on the side of the bath, whispering words of acceptance between each contraction. I knew I just had to ride it out. At one point I started singing, 'Shake your groove thing', in between contractions. We all laughed until another contraction propelled me onto my knees. When it became too intense to bear, I felt I heard a voice say, 'I'm holding your hands.' I visualised Jesus sitting there with me. It was as if someone was giving me the strength that I lacked in that moment.

For a while I was able to breathe, to sleep again. I felt like I slept for hours but it must have only been a couple of minutes. Then I started grunting, suddenly alert. I felt my baby's head move down and looked up at everyone in surprise. I was having this baby! It took quite a while for Adam's head to come down. He went out and in, and out and in and eventually, midwife Lynne suggested I get out of the bath. At that point his head came half-way out and then with one more push he flew out into Lynne's hands.

I stared at my precious new baby in disbelief. 'I did it!' I pushed a baby out and I didn't need surgery. The euphoria was inexplicable! Our eyes met and we fell instantly in love but I wasn't possessive or hyper-vigilant, like I had been with Liam and even Daniel. I felt relaxed in the bond we had. And it continues to this day.

Adam's birth gave me some incredible gifts. It somehow made me feel stronger. I no longer allow people to take my power away. Also, the memory of those first moments is very precious. It brings warmth to my heart every time I think about it. In many ways Adam gave others a gift too – those who have not had the experiences I have had and who believe they are somehow faulty. This makes me feel very sad when I can see so plainly now that all the interference and lack of respect for my role as chief decision-maker in my care was what caused the trauma with Liam's birth. It was all so unnecessary. I would like nothing more than for all women to feel like I did the day Adam was born. To find yourself on the birth front is to find out who you are and what you are made of.

Jill's story

I first met Saira at the beginning of her second pregnancy. She was very anxious as she had found her previous labour and birth difficult and frightening. Her first pregnancy had been uneventful until she had pre-labour rupture of membranes at 37 weeks. Her labour had been induced 24 hours later, firstly with prostaglandin pessaries, then with a syntocinon drip. Once on the drip she had progressed very quickly (from 3cm dilated to birth of Alliyah within about one and a half hours). She had had a perineal tear which had initially been sutured in the birth room, but continued bleeding which had necessitated repair in theatre under spinal anaesthesia. She also had a haematoma.

Saira had felt traumatised by the birth, mainly as she felt the midwife had not listened to her when she said she needed to push and that the baby was coming. Following Alliyah's birth, Saira had seen our consultant midwife to discuss her experience and when she became pregnant for the second time was allocated to the caseload team (providing one-to-one care) during pregnancy, labour and birth and the postnatal period by a known, named midwife.

At our first meeting I listened to Saira carefully, so that between us we could find out if we could work together. Saira had not started to make any plans for her second delivery as she was still coming to terms with Alliyah's birth. During our early appointments Saira talked over and over her previous birth. I was able to give her time to do this without rushing and helped her to identify the things that would be important for her in her next labour. Above all Saira had a great need to know she would be listened to, that her feelings, physical and emotional, would be taken notice of. I reassured her that I would listen and that if I was unavailable my colleagues would fully understand Saira's needs.

We began to discuss Saira's next labour in more detail and what would help her. We visited the delivery suite at the local obstetric unit, considered homebirth and waterbirth and Saira decided that a waterbirth in hospital was her choice. This was a really important step for Saira in taking back control of her choices. As a midwife I felt I was able to walk alongside Saira on her decision-making journey, pointing out the possibilities while encouraging her to make her choices. We spent time with her husband and birth supporter, Ali, looking at the physical process of labour and coping mechanisms such as positions, massage, and breathing, providing them both with skills that they could use in labour, particularly while still at home.

At 38 weeks Saira's waters broke early one Sunday morning. I visited her at home and made sure all was well. The liquor draining was clear, Saira felt well and the baby's heart rate was normal. Saira was beginning to have some period-type pains and wanted to stay at home to await events. Later that afternoon I visited the family again, Saira was having strong contractions every 10 minutes or so; liquor remained clear. I asked Saira what she wanted to do.

There didn't seem any reason to go to hospital yet, but Saira needed to be the one to make that decision. She asked me to examine her as her main fear of staying at home would be that labour progressed too quickly. I found that her cervix was 3cm dilated, almost fully effaced, soft and stretchy. This reassured Saira and she felt happy for me to leave her once more until things progressed.

A few hours later, I answered the telephone to a panicky Saira. She was having much stronger contractions every four minutes and wanted to go to hospital. I arranged to meet her on the delivery suite, but when Saira and Ali arrived, all contractions stopped. We carried out a fetal heart monitoring due to Saira's waters having broken and discussed what she wanted to do. She wanted to go home and wait. I made sure she knew she could ring me at any time and off they went.

The following morning at 6am Saira rang to say contractions were becoming strong and regular again, could I visit in an hour? At 6.30 she rang to cancel the visit, then at 6.45 rang to request I visit straight away! I arrived at 7.10 and the contractions were quite strong, with four occurring in every 25 minutes. At Saira's request I carried out a further vaginal examination and her cervix was now 5cm dilated. Saira decided it was time to go to hospital as she wanted to get in the pool.

When we arrived Saira was offered intravenous antibiotic cover due to her being more than 24 hours post-ruptured membranes, and she took up this offer, having her first dose while I carried out fetal continuous cardiotocography (due to more than 24 hours since rupture of membranes) and began filling the pool. However, by the time the intravenous antibiotic had run through and the fetal cardiotocograph was completed, contractions had slowed down to two to three in 15 minutes and were variable in strength. I encouraged Saira to mobilise, and she and Ali left the delivery suite to wander round the hospital and get a drink, etc.

An hour later they returned. Contractions were now regular, one every five minutes, strong to palpate. We finished filling the pool and Saira got in and immediately found it very relaxing. However, after 20 minutes it became obvious that contractions were spacing out again.

Thirty minutes later, Saira left the pool to use the toilet, and then got back in the pool but her contractions remained spaced out.

At 12 noon, she requested a further vaginal examination as she was feeling worried that labour was stopping. The presenting part was lower in the pelvis, cervix 7cm dilated, but contractions were one every seven to eight minutes. I suggested that Saira leave the pool and mobilise and the contractions became more regular almost immediately.

During her labour I listened carefully to Saira, asked what she wanted and needed, and respected her wishes. In return Saira also listened to me and my suggestions – going out for a walk, leaving the pool to mobilise. The relationship we had developed during her pregnancy meant that we could trust and be honest with each other.

While she continued to move around, Saira told me she wanted to start using entonox as her contractions were feeling much stronger. This was a good positive sign that labour was progressing well, I encouraged and supported her to continue mobilising with Ali's help even when the second dose of intravenous antibiotics was running.

Within 30 minutes Saira was having three contractions every 15 minutes and they were strong and longer lasting. Therefore, I began reheating the pool. Saira sounded as if she was making spontaneous pushing efforts at peak of contractions. I never asked her if she felt she needed to push, I relied on what I could hear and see. I feel that asking a woman if she feels like pushing can sound as if you think she should be pushing, and then the woman starts to push because she thinks it is the right thing to do, rather than listening to her body.

Saira quickly returned to the pool which she found very comforting. She was becoming more distressed with each contraction and needed all the support Ali and I could give. She tried many different positions in the pool before finally taking up a kneeling position which she found comfortable, despite becoming more distressed. She was obviously pushing spontaneously at the peak of her contractions, but there was nothing visible at this point.

After about 15 minutes there were obvious external signs of descent – the perineum stretching and vulva gaping. Saira turned to semi-sitting, supported from behind by Ali.

Three minutes later the baby's head was born, quickly followed by his body and Safira put her hands down to help lift him out of the water and onto her skin. She and Ali shed tears as they exclaimed over their new son.

Fifteen minutes later Saira wanted to leave the pool. The cord was fairly short and as it had stopped pulsating, it was clamped and then Ali cut it, which made getting out of the pool a little easier. Once comfortable in a reclining chair Saira was pleased that her new baby wanted to start suckling at her breast, but soon felt some stomach pains and the need to push. Ten minutes later the placenta and membranes were delivered.

Mohammed breastfed very well following his birth and has continued to do so. Saira is really pleased with this as she struggled to breastfeed Alliyah, Saira says this is because she had so little time to 'bond' in those first few hours, ending up expressing and giving by bottle for several months.

Saira had sustained a small first-degree tear and a small labial graze during the birth, but did not need any stitches – she was very pleased, but this just goes to show how important it is for a woman to listen and respond to her body's response to spontaneous labour. Undoubtedly, Saira's lack of perineal trauma has contributed to the speed of her recovery after the birth. Her family have told me she is a different woman, able to care for her baby and be part of the whole family, rather than last time when her pain and unhappiness made it much more difficult for her.

Saira tells me herself that she can't believe birth can be like this. She told me that knowing and trusting her caregiver had a huge impact on her ability to listen to her body and for helping labour progress. She thinks every woman should be able to know their midwife.

As a midwife, knowing the women I care for makes my job easier. I don't have to start making a new relationship when a woman is in advanced labour and risk disturbing her labour's rhythm. By having time to know each other beforehand we can discuss her hopes, fears and plans and develop an understanding of each other without the added pressure of labour. Labour and birth become an instinctive process for both of us, a dance we follow even though we don't remember learning the steps.

CHAPTER 4

Tales from birth centres and caseload schemes

Sarah's story (midwife)

I am a birth centre midwife. I knew right from the first day of my midwifery training that my midwifery home would be here. I can 'do' high risk and I have done my time in a consultant unit, but that's not true midwifery to me. So as soon as I was able, I came home to my local birth centre (where I gave birth to one of my own children). It is a small unprepossessing one-storey building in a small town 12 miles from the consultant unit.

I work with midwives who looked after me when I was pregnant and I look after my fellow midwives who are pregnant now. And I look after women who came to me in their first pregnancy, who then became friends and came back again with their next pregnancy. And I hope the next and the next.

Working a shift in the birth centre means that you never know what you will be doing. The phone is busy with questions ranging from, 'What time are the visiting hours', to which the answer is very straightforward, to, 'I don't feel quite right', to which the answer is a series of questions usually followed by a invitation to 'Come in and let's check you over'. In the seven postnatal beds will be women and their babies who may have had any sort of birth from planned caesarean sections to waterbirths. Most will be breastfeeding and some will need the support and guidance that the birth centre is renowned for locally. All are given a chance to feel cared for and to have time to adjust to the newness of being a parent for the first, second, third or whatever time.

In the day time, midwives are in and out of the birth centre and there is friendly banter between them, the healthcare assistants, hotel services staff and clerical staff. It is like a family that has relationships which are usually supportive but can be strained when situations, personalities and sometimes ethos's clash. When one of the midwives left the birth pool tap running and the water was ankle deep in the labour rooms (and yes there was a woman in labour), everyone rallied round to mop up the flood and, messy as it was, it was taken in good humour, although of course the midwife will have to put up with a certain amount of ribbing for ever after.

Dropping into the birth centre today found me unexpectedly helping a student midwife to record her third birth. As I was going up the corridor, I met the a midwife coming towards me at a run pushing a fold-up wheelchair saying, 'There is a woman in the car park trying to give birth in her car!'

I do an about turn and run out to the car park to find a woman on the back seat of her car clearly in advanced labour but, on quick inspection, there is no sign of a baby yet. The woman manages to get out of the car into the wheelchair and we zoom along the path back to the birth centre and into the labour room. We have now been joined by a student midwife, the woman's mother and the woman's partner.

I help the woman onto the bed as we haven't managed to prepare the room, while my colleague sorts out the resuscitaire, the delivery pack and the woman's notes. A quick scan of the notes tells us that the student midwife is welcome to be there and within the next 10 minutes the atmosphere has gone from panic stations to calm. The woman is now kneeling on the mat on the floor, her head in her partner's arms and her mother by her side. Soon we can see the baby's head as we look in the mirror we have placed under her. She's pushing so well and although she says nothing is happening we reassure her that her baby will soon be born.

Thirty minutes later, the student midwife helps the woman to breathe her baby's head out, quickly followed by the body and then passes the baby though the mother's legs and onto a clean towel in front of her and her partner. Then follows the best bit. The mother reaches down and picks her baby up and holds her close. The father kneels next to them and puts his arm around her and together they stare at their baby and start to touch her, stroking her hair, letting her hold their finger in her tiny hand. Each time the feeling of seeing the start of a new family is startlingly powerful and amazingly beautiful.

Of course this sort of dramatic birth doesn't happen every day and for me the best births are the ones that are looked forward to for nine months. Those births where you are there right at the beginning from the moment when you meet the newly pregnant woman for the first time, and are then there when she labours and gives birth. These births are for me the icing on the midwifery cake. And women who have their own midwife with them for the whole of the birth process, from early pregnancy, through labour and birth and the early weeks of new parenthood appreciate this special relationship. They send cards telling us so, such as, 'Just a quick note to say a very large thank-you for making the birth of my baby a happy occasion instead of the frightening experience I was expecting. Your assistance was exceptional and perfect for my needs. Thank you for being there.'

I had looked after Kate in her first pregnancy and she had a straightforward and relatively quick birth for a first time mother. During this pregnancy the relationship we had started during her first pregnancy and birth grew over the next nine months. As her due date approached we talked about what her hopes were for this birth and whether there was anything that she would like to do or not do that was different from last time. Then, as her due date came, I went away on holiday for a week and jokingly told her she had to wait until I came back to give birth. When I came back her baby had still not arrived. I was working in the unit and had just helped a women birth her first baby in the birthing pool when the phone rang. It was Paul on the phone saying Kate had been for a long walk in the morning and they had climbed over two or three stiles and by lunchtime her contractions had started.

'You know you said to stay at home until Kate was having contractions that were coming every 5 minutes and she couldn't talk through them, well she's been doing that for the last hour and she's got her TENS on and she says she's probably only 2cm dilated but can she come in and be checked.'

'Of course you can come in – and it sounds like things are really happening, that's great.'

Because I know Kate and Paul so well, I know that Kate really wants to have this baby in the birthing pool, that she wants to push out her placenta herself and that they want the baby to have Vitamin K by injection. I don't need to have a conversation about her wishes for this labour and birth as we've already done this. There is time enough for me to let the pool water drain away from the previous birth and for the pool to be cleaned and to start refilling before Kate and Paul arrive. Greeting them at the door is like welcoming old friends and that's because they are now old friends. I have the labour room ready with the mat on the floor with the big bean bag to lean on, the lights on low and some background music plays on the CD player. We go into the room together and Kate settles herself on the mat, while Paul sorts out the practical stuff, putting bags down and finding Kate's notes, turning off his mobile so that he can concentrate on Kate and what she needs. I am in the background, doing the midwife things as unobtrusively as I can, temperature, blood pressure, pulse, abdominal palpation, fetal heart rate. I start the notes and I write them as a story.

'Kate has been having contractions since lunchtime. They have got stronger and closer together since then and they are now coming every three or four minutes. Her baby has been moving around and Kate says her waters haven't broken yet. Paul is rubbing Kate's back for some of the contractions.'

Kate is focused and inward, she doesn't talk very much except to ask for sips of water. She is in her own space and although I know she can hear my words of encouragement and admiration at her ability to breathe through her contractions, I do not want her to come out of her space to interact with me and so I keep my voice low. Time passes and I can see Kate's labour move on. After one particularly intense contraction Kate asks to get into the pool and so we gather a few things and move into the pool room. The overhead light is off (nasty florescent thing), and the underwater light shines through the water and makes dancing patterns on the ceiling. There is no need to examine Kate as her body is starting to want to push her baby out. There is no great urgency and Kate is still quite calm and relaxed. I let my second midwife know that the baby is on its way and she stays outside the room knowing that a second person at this stage can subtly change the highly charged atmosphere. Gradually Kate's body decides that it is time for the baby to start moving down and very soon I can see the dark hair of the baby's head just waving about in the water as Kate pushes. A few more pushes and the head starts to emerge smoothly but with just enough time for Kate to respond to my reminder to just breathe and try not to push. With the next two contractions Kate breathes the baby's head out and then the shoulders and body follow. The baby appears to almost swim through Kate's legs and I gently bring her to the surface and give her to Kate. The three of us are silent as we revel in this most incredible moment as Kate and Paul meet their newborn daughter.

The story doesn't end with the birth of course but my shift ends and I know I can happily leave Kate and her baby to my colleague who is on the night shift. My colleague shares my feeling of intense satisfaction, she is happy for me as a midwife and for the new parents, and I go home to share the news with my family who are always keen to hear stories from my working day, even though I'm sure they sometimes hear rather more detail than they bargained for!

Tomorrow I will see Kate again, do the neonatal examination for her baby and in the days and weeks to come watch the re-shaping of their family from three to four. Then I will gradually draw away as the relationship moves on from midwife back to friend, until the next time... And that's as it should be as I have a busy caseload and have many other pregnant women to care for.

Sarah's story (Mother)

My baby girl is seven weeks and three days old today. I can honestly say the days since she arrived have been the most content and fulfilled of my life. Twenty two months ago I gave birth to our son, William. He was much wanted and we eagerly anticipated his arrival. I went into labour on Sunday 3rd December at lunchtime. By midnight the contractions were every five or so minutes and we went to hospital. I was 2cm dilated so told to go home. We returned to hospital in the morning and William was finally born in the birthing pool at 7.30pm. It had been a very long day and not at all as we had expected. I had a third degree tear and went to theatre to be sutured.

The following four days were spent on a very busy post-natal ward. I left hospital on pain killers and antibiotics, weary and with bleeding nipples. Once home, the next few weeks were awful. A combination of many things led to me stopping breast feeding at four weeks and seeking counselling. The following April I had a small operation to the scar tissue of the tear. Finally, five months later, I began to feel like myself again and eventually I began to truly enjoy my son.

At the time I vowed I would never have another baby. The experience and what it reduced me to was not one I wished to repeat. However, as the months passed, I changed my mind.

When I found out I was pregnant on Christmas Eve 2007, I was delighted. My husband was over the moon and we couldn't wait to meet our new little one. However, at the back of my mind was the prospect of labour, delivery, breast feeding and the first few weeks with a newborn; I dreaded all of it.

I discussed my fears with the midwife at my first antenatal appointment. She immediately referred me to Sheena. I was able to discuss my previous experience fully both from a physical and emotional level. For the first time I felt a professional was taking me seriously and I felt my experience was truly being listened to rather than ignored. This in itself was so cathartic. Sheena assured me that birth could and should be a wonderful, positive experience. I longed to believe her but for me, birth had been lonely, frightening, humiliating, disempowering and agonising.

Sheena placed me with the case load midwifery team. I can't even remember how pregnant I was when I met Jill but that was the moment everything changed! Jill took over my antenatal care and visited our home many times during the rest of the pregnancy. William enjoyed her visits and it was good to talk to her about his delivery. Jill put my mind at ease by talking me through possible reasons for the problems I had encountered and helped me to be proactive in addressing them. After much discussion with Al, we decided that we would try and have a waterbirth again. This was discussed with Jill and a birth plan was written. Every aspect from the first contraction to the delivery of the placenta and the first feeds were discussed, a luxury I had not had the first time round. Due to Sheena and Jill's contacts, we sought the advice of a homeopath. The remedies she prescribed helped me in pregnancy and we hired a kit for the labour. I had a wonderful pregnancy and felt very well both physically and emotionally. As the due date approached, I felt calm and prepared, rather than terrified as I had thought I would.

The due date arrived and contractions began mid-afternoon. It was not Jill's on call day but I had met Anita from her team and happily rang her. Her advice was to relax and try and get some sleep to see how things progressed. They slowed down and I did get a few hours sleep. The following morning, again on Anita's advice, we took a short walk to my mum's. The contractions suddenly began coming thick and fast. As the time came for us to leave William at my mum's I felt a flood of panic. I was terrified at the prospect of enduring hours of labour followed by weeks of pain. I cried as we left our little boy and returned to our house. The contractions continued to intensify and I put off ringing Anita. In my head I was determined to hang on as long as I could just in case I heard again the dreaded words, 'You're only 2cm'. We eventually rang her at about 1pm. Bless her, she came from her shopping in Accrington to our home to see how we were. It was fantastic to have a midwife come to our home rather than trail to hospital not knowing whether we'd be sent home or not. This time, I was 6cm and we were on our way to the hospital within minutes of her visit.

The journey was... fun?! We got stuck behind a learner as we came off the motorway and I was laughing during contractions even though they were pretty sore by then. We parked and walked up to delivery.We were laughing in the lift at the prospect of us getting stuck and Al having to deliver the baby by himself. However, we arrived on delivery to be greeted by Anita who had the pool ready. I couldn't wait to get in and instantly felt relaxed and at home. What a difference to William's arrival. The waiting around and being moved from room to room, not knowing whether I was going to be able to get in the birth pool due to staffing problems, emergency sections and a crowded delivery suite.

A few minutes later, Jill arrived, despite it not being her day on call. She said she didn't want to miss it. I will never forget that. It was so touching to know she genuinely wanted to be there for the arrival of our little one. Anita had been wonderful at settling us in and now Jill took over.

As the contractions began to really take hold, Jill talked me through every one. She spoke calmly and reminded me over and over that I would soon see my baby. She talked to me about William. She chatted to Al. She got Al involved and talked both of us through exactly what was happening to my body. She helped me find a position that was comfortable. She made suggestions to help the discomfort. In between contractions I was able to chat and laugh along with them. We even had our photos taken, enjoying the moment. She helped me to breathe through my contractions and the way she got me to relax was the best pain reliever.

It was just the three of us. Nobody came in and out of the room. The equipment she needed to monitor me and the baby was to hand and all worked as it should. There was no rush and no checking of the clock. Jill supported me and helped Al to support me. Instead of feeling alone and vulnerable, I felt looked after and completely in control. Instead of feeling frightened I felt calm and confident. Instead of feeling like I was doing something wrong and that I needed to speed the labour up, I felt she had all the time in the world for us. Instead of being in agony and losing my mind with the pain, I felt each contraction come and go and coped with them with their help one at a time. It was entirely different to William's birth.

As I began to lose the ability to relax through the contractions I started to use gas and air. The contractions slowed. I began to get impatient. Jill suggested I get out for a walk. I did and the contractions picked up again. I got back into the pool and within a few more minutes I knew my baby was coming. The pain was suddenly so intense and I remember hearing Jill tell Al to pull the buzzer and tell me to slow down. It was no good. I didn't feel like I was pushing at all, instead it was our baby girl pushing with all her might to get out. She arrived in seconds and I looked down to see William had a little sister.

We had more photos of the first few minutes with our daughter then Al cut the cord. We got out and Al had skin to skin contact with her while the placenta was delivered. I was supported completely through the first feed. Our daughter was weighed and dressed. I didn't need any stitches and, instead of going to theatre, had a lovely bath! We had sandwiches and cups of tea. There was no rush. We were simply allowed to enjoy those first precious hours while being supported and cared for by a wonderful midwife.

Jill settled us onto the ward. Other fantastic midwives supported the feeding through the night. We came home the following day. I could go to the toilet, have a shower, bath my baby, dress my baby, walk, get in the car and sit down, all pain-free. It was amazing.

During the next four weeks, I did encounter problems feeding Isla similar to those I had with William. However, Jill was there to ensure I got the right medication when I needed it and to get the advice. Seven weeks on, I am still feeding Isla myself and loving the privilege.

The whole experience was simply wonderful. Everything was perfect and the fantastic start has led to a fantastic few weeks for us.

I cannot even begin to compare the experiences of the births of my children. They are so starkly different. Is this simply because William was my first and I didn't know what to expect? Not at all. I believe that Isla's birth was so wonderful for one reason only and that is the quality of the care we received. I received wonderful emotional care from Sheena, practical care from Annette, and feeding care from Sue. Because Jill knew us and we knew her, we felt like a friend was in the delivery room with us. This goes a long way towards calming a labouring woman's mental and emotional state. She was the best pain relief. Because of the nature of Jill's role, I know she could give me complete one-to-one support throughout the whole labour and in the crucial hours and days afterwards. The care was consistent and continuous. This is essential if women are to have positive births, succeed with establishing breast feeding and be well.

We were treated like royalty and are left with only the most wonderful memories rather than painful scars. We are so thankful to all the professionals who we were fortunate enough to have help us.

Trudy's story

Emma was 17 years old when she became pregnant. She was visually impaired and found it difficult at times getting to places and finding her way around. She was very anxious in unfamiliar surroundings and therefore relied on her family for support.

At her booking appointment the midwife had recognised Emma would benefit from extra support during her pregnancy and referred her to our caseload team. When I first met Emma she was living with her parents and brothers who were all very supportive of her. However, before she became pregnant she had boarded at a college for the visually impaired and had become more independent and gained some confidence while she had been away from home. It was important to Emma to maintain her independence as much as possible.

During her stay at college Emma had developed a relationship with Sam. They hadn't been seeing each other for long when Emma discovered she was pregnant. Sam was also visually impaired and did not live locally. Emma's parents were upset, surprised and shocked by the news of Emma's pregnancy but were supportive. When Emma returned home Sam soon followed and moved in with her family.

I arranged to see Emma at home for our first visit. Emma's mum was there and Emma was quiet, shy and nervous, allowing her mum to do most of the talking at first. It was obvious to me that Emma and her mum had a very close relationship and her mum was very protective of her. We discussed her pregnancy, the choices she had relating to her care and the group activities available to young mums to be. Emma and I felt she would benefit from one-to-one midwifery care and support as she wasn't comfortable in a group environment, and would require someone to attend with her to help her, as visual aids were not available at these groups. With one-to-one care we could address all Emma's needs. It was important to Emma and Sam to prepare for becoming a family together, ensuring a positive role for Sam but also allowing Emma's mum to support the couple.

Following Emma's scan at 20 weeks, possible fetal abnormalities were highlighted. Emma had to attend further screening, an amniocentesis, and was seen at a specialist centre for further scans. The baby was diagnosed with an obstructed bowel which would possibly need surgical intervention soon after the birth. This led to a very anxious period during her pregnancy. Emma was reassured that if she had any anxieties or concerns she could contact a midwife who knew her any time and she wouldn't need to explain her case every time.

Emma's mum had recently decided to return to work with her children now growing up and Emma moving off to college. This meant that she was sometimes unable to accompany Emma to her appointments, and Sam continued with his college studies so was unavailable. I therefore stepped in to help and was able to attend with her. Car journeys to and from hospital appointments gave Emma and I time on our own to talk, become familiar with each other and build up a good trusting relationship. As our relationship developed, Emma openly talked about her feelings, her excitement for the future, apprehension for the birth and her fears of being a mum with a disability. Emma had always felt that her family had protected her and as part of that they had been at the forefront of conversations and decisions, and Emma had very often hidden behind her mum. When I attended appointments with her I encouraged her to ask questions and ensured she was aware of her choices and that she was at the centre of her care. I could see her becoming more relaxed around people and becoming more confident. She had good support from her family but she wanted 'to be the mum' and she wanted her mum 'to be the nan'. She didn't want to have to rely on her mum to care for the baby.

Emma took great care of herself during her pregnancy, eating healthily and getting regular exercise. Emma and Sam prepared well for the baby, buying something each week until they were ready. I visited her at home and we prepared for her labour, birth and caring for a baby. We discussed signs of labour, coping strategies and positions for labour so she could make informed choices. We also talked about her mum and boyfriend's roles as birthing partners, and in infant feeding and baby care. We practised bathing the baby and changing nappies, using a baby doll, and sterilising equipment and making up feeds so Emma could gain confidence and be happy with her ability to do these tasks. Together, Emma, Sam and I visited the delivery suite, allowing time for Emma and Sam to become familiar with the environment and the equipment in the rooms. This also gave Emma and Sam the opportunity to identify anything we could do or change to help them. We found lighting in the rooms was a problem as it hindered Emma and Sam further with their vision, so we still had reduced lighting but kept some lights on for their comfort. We also spent some time on the post-natal ward as the paediatricians had asked Emma to stay so the baby could be observed to assess if surgery was required. Following this visit Emma and I prepared a birth plan with the choices Emma had made.

As it got closer to Emma's due date she became increasingly nervous. We talked about different scenarios and the importance of remaining positive.

When Emma was 41 weeks pregnant, she rang to say she had started having contractions but they were irregular and she was coping well at home.

I was able to reassure her and advise her to continue until her contractions became regular, suggesting relaxing in the bath and a having back massage. Several hours later Emma rang, her contractions were now regular and she was feeling uncomfortable. I had arranged to assess Emma's onset of labour at home as she wanted to stay at home as long as possible.

When I arrived at her house all her family were in, her brothers tucked away in their rooms out of the way, her nervous dad pacing the lounge and Emma, Sam and her mum in her bedroom. Emma had been in and out of the bath and Sam had been doing an excellent job of massaging her lower back.

When first examined she was 4cm dilated and her contractions were four minutes apart. Emma was really relaxed and focused. She decided she wanted to go to the delivery suite as she felt increasingly uncomfortable at home, and when we arrived there we were able to use a room Emma was familiar with. Emma remained upright throughout her labour, standing, sitting in the rocking chair, and resting over the bed on all fours. Her labour progressed well and she remained calm and relaxed, with plenty of praise, encouragement and reassurance from Sam, her mum and myself. Abigail was born a short time later, and Sam was able to cut the cord with guidance, which was something he had wanted to do but thought he wouldn't be 'allowed' to do. Emma was overwhelmed at her achievement and lovingly cradled her daughter in her arms.

Three days following her birth Abigail was transferred to a children's hospital to undergo surgery. I was able to contact the hospital and arrange with staff for Emma to stay with Abigail as Emma's mum was finding it difficult to provide transport for Emma and Sam and maintain her work commitments. Also Emma did not want to be separated from her new baby. Throughout the three-week period of Abigail's hospital stay, Emma and I kept in contact via mobile phone. Emma was grateful for this additional support; she rang to let me know how Abigail was doing and sometimes she just rang to have a good chat about how she was feeling.

Emma and Sam had been very nervous about their lack of experience with parenting skills and the added stress of their visual impairment. However, they were determined to learn and become good parents. Since then, Emma and Sam are coping well, they are gaining confidence and enjoying being parents. They continue to live with Emma's parents but require little support with baby care. Abigail is now a healthy and thriving baby.

With some extra support Emma was able to achieve a good birthing experience, she felt there was always someone there who would listen to her and who she could ask questions. She was able to make her own choices and had felt confident with the support she received.

I feel Emma, Sam, Emma's mum, myself and the doctors worked well as a team ensuring Emma's needs were met and enabling her to gain confidence in her ability to make decisions and remain at the centre of her care. This story demonstrates how much good communication, trust, friendship and partnership can achieve.

CHAPTER 5

Tales of loss

Kate and Sheena, facilitated by Gill

The first time the story below was told, it was as a dramatic performance to the third international UK normal birth research conference in 2006. Kate and Sheena were asked to do this by Professor Soo Downe to highlight the fact that doing normal, out-of-hospital childbirth may end up exposing mother and midwife to litigation, because this choice is not seen as the standard, 'safest' option, despite evidence to the contrary. Soo was particularly keen for midwives to recognise the need to be courageous in facing this possible outcome. The argument was that facing fear of litigation may reduce the risk of defensive practice: once the worst has been faced and accepted, there is nothing more to fear.

Kate's part of the story illustrates the fact that, often, women are caught up in litigation in a way that can be as damaging as the original trauma suffered in unexpectedly pathological childbirth. No-one is a winner in this circumstance. Sheena and Kate show in stark and clear-sighted detail what this experience feels like, and how it is possible to work through it, overcome it, and still maintain faith in normal birth processes, and in mutually respectful relationships.

The mother, the midwife and litigation: Coming full circle

They met on a winter's morning in 2004. Kate was a 30-year-old woman who had recently returned from four years living in the East, working in refugee communities with her Tibetan husband. Although she had grown up in Lancashire she was living in Swansea, South Wales, working full time in a hostel for homeless people, when she became pregnant with her first child in July 2004.

Sheena was a community midwife with experience of homebirth and 10 years in a GP maternity home (similar to a birth centre) where there was no medical cover.

For Kate, choosing a homebirth seemed quite normal: she was born at home, as were her siblings. Her mother is Dutch and so home did not seem so unusual. She had read up on the subject and had direct experience of how things can be in hospital. Kate had been by her younger sister's side when she was taken for an emergency caesarean, the direct result of over- intervention.

For Sheena, homebirth was the ultimate practice for the use of her midwifery skills. She had worked in a GP maternity home where there was no intervention, and had seen the benefits that brought. More than this, her desire to assist women in their choice was and still is her passion.

Kate had received her antenatal care in another area, where she was booked for a homebirth. She wasn't given GP cover but the midwives were very supportive and discussed the homebirth guidance and support with Kate. However Kate lived in a house shared with two men, both smokers, attached to the hostel where she worked. When a friend suggested that Kate move to a more beautiful peaceful area close to where her parents lived, to stay and give birth in the friend's spare house, Kate wrote to the head of midwifery to explore the possibility of transferring the homebirth option there.

In the last month of the pregnancy Kate moved up to the Ribble Valley and met Sheena, the midwife who was going to provide her care. Sheena had been asked to care for Kate by her manager, who had read Kate's letter out during a team meeting.

Kate and Sheena's story

Kate: Sheena and I clicked right from the start. She was so open and respectful, and interested in me as a person. I trusted her and was delighted that she would be with me on this amazing journey into motherhood.

Sheena: I sat on the floor in Kate's home and she offered me Tibetan tea. Kate told me her story of pregnancy so far, and her desire to birth at home. It was Kate's first baby and she was so excited. I didn't meet Cheophel, her husband but heard all about him, and felt privileged and happy to be their midwife. I told Kate I would try to be available for the birth by being on call for the necessary three to four weeks. Normal procedures were followed. There wasn't much discussion about the choice of home delivery as the decision had been made in Wales and discussion had taken place there.

Kate: I didn't think to ask lots of questions about travel time and distances to hospital: I assumed that if the midwives were happy to take me on, and had done the same for other women, it wasn't an issue.

Sheena: I didn't go into any great detail about distance from hospital, etc. as I rightly or wrongly assumed Kate knew how far the hospital was. It wasn't my practice to do so, as I had a worked for 10 years in a maternity unit that was quite near to where Kate lived, and transfer hadn't been a problem. Kate wanted a homebirth, she was very healthy and happy, and ready to meet her baby.

Kate called Sheena the morning she went into labour and Sheena attended shortly afterwards.

Sheena: Kate's labour was amazing; she was active and alert, calm and serene, and very excited. Cheophel and Lucy (Kate's friend) were present, and providing wonderful support.

I loved caring for Kate. I remember her movements, her smile, the lambs in the fields outside and the loving touches of her birth partners. She was agile, and worked with her labour like a strong, proud woman.

When there was spontaneous rupture of membranes, Sheena performed a vaginal examination to exclude cord prolapse (practice at the time). Kate was standing for the examination, and her cervix was found to be fully dilated. The head however, was still above the ischial spines, and Kate had no desire to push. The second midwife listened to the fetal heart, and there was acute prolonged bradycardia. The emergency services were called.

Kate: I had felt strong and centred, but now I started to feel powerless. I knew things were not going as they should, but there seemed to be nothing I could do about it. I tried to remain calm, to not panic, to breathe deeply. It was my first child, so I had no experience to measure it against. I looked to Sheena for guidance; she was my anchor. Time seemed to stretch out and slow down, I recall an incredible sense of clarity but huge waves of fear rising within.

Sheena: The fetal heart beat was still 60bpm. Immediately my feelings lunged from fear, hope and an urgency to protect. The fear was the strongest sense, and increased with each passing second. I couldn't do anything. Kate was mobile, so changing her position was a constant thing, and the baby couldn't be born yet. When the baby's heart beat increased slightly, hope returned but disappeared as quickly as it came. I knew emergency services had been called so in terms of 'correct procedure', all was in order. But it was not. Reality was the person in front of me, Kate, who trusted me implicitly and whom I couldn't help. I will never forget Kate's eyes, looking into mine, searching for something that I found so hard to give. I wanted to say, 'It's good Kate, you are going to be fine,' but I couldn't because I wasn't sure that it was. How could I lie to her? Words that have always come so easily to me during my career were now unsuitable and inappropriate. Neither could I say, 'I am sorry,' as I would have done had fetal death occurred, because the possible outcome couldn't be spoken about. I had an incredible overwhelming desire to take Kate in my arms and make her safe, or to somehow speed up the birth. But I could do neither.

The ambulance arrived 40 minutes after the call to the hospital. A local GP was present, but couldn't assist. The procedure at the time was still the 'Flying Squad', where an ambulance was called as an emergency, but it called at the hospital to collect the necessary clinicians. The communication between the hospital and ambulance control initiated a response to send one ambulance with obstetrician, midwife, paediatrician and full resuscitation equipment. The room Kate was in was small, and yet the paediatrician began to set up the equipment, and the doctor urgently proceeded to examine Kate.

Kate: The house seemed to have been invaded; people upstairs, downstairs, on the stairs, in every room; women and also men that I didn't know; disembodied voices; glimpses of uniforms. The registrar examined me and didn't inspire confidence or trust; she seemed authoritarian towards me, but scattered in herself. I looked to Sheena, trying to keep the connection, trying to find the direction. My impression was that she had been blocked out by the registrar who had taken over control, and yet didn't seem in control. It felt as if I had been cut loose, adrift on a sea of emotions I hadn't been prepared to negotiate.

Sheena: The ambulance was here, and familiar faces. Fetal heart still 60. The doctor was experienced, the midwife a trusted colleague, and the paediatrician was here with his equipment. An examination was made, questions asked, and there was a flurry of activity. The doctor wasn't happy to try to deliver the baby, and asked for Kate's transfer in. Another ambulance was needed, as Kate and the equipment could not fit in one ambulance. The baby could have been born during the journey. Despair increased and fear intensified. There was confusion and uncertainty. Cheophel looked so afraid, yet I wondered if he really understood the seriousness of the events. How could I make him feel better? I couldn't speak his language and even if I could, I was unable to say the right thing. I touched his arm but I couldn't smile. Kate asked, 'Should I push?' 'No' says the doctor, 'the baby's position is not good, the head is too high.'

I knew this was so, as I had examined Kate. Kate looks to me not the doctor. Eyes burning into mine. What could I do? Fetal heart still 60bpm. Despair.

The second ambulance arrived, and transfer began a further 44 minutes later.

There was some relief when the second ambulance arrived but only because something could progress. The fear was still strong, what was to be?

Kate: I started to feel annoyed with everyone else apart from Sheena; I just wanted them to go away and to get back to the birthing we had been dealing with together. I felt that I was no longer present as a person any more; that the whole birthing had been taken out of my hands. I was no longer a woman giving birth to a baby, but a body out of which a baby had to be extracted. I was both acutely aware of myself and at the same time felt entirely disconnected from myself. There was an almost tangible feeling of alienation, which I can only describe as an out-of-body experience as I observed all of those things happening to me, but without my being involved. My body was led down the stairs, my nakedness barely concealed as I stepped out into the spring day on to the street. The hospital is 12 miles away, and it is peak time. Transfer to hospital began, with the assistance of the blue light.

Kate was with Cheophel, the doctor, Sheena and another midwife who came in the first ambulance. The second ambulance followed with the paediatrician and the equipment. Cheophel was sat at the bottom of the stretcher that held Kate. Sheena was stood close, trying to listen to the fetal heart. The other midwife recorded the activity. Kate wanted to push during the journey.

Sheena: The journey was so difficult for Kate. The fetal heart rate was still 60bpm. She was desperate and scared, and I could sense such sadness in Cheophel who I knew understood the level of urgency. When Kate wanted to push, I could see the baby's head advancing; lots of black hair. From his position, Cheophel could see too, and looked at me for a solution. As I would normally do, I encouraged Kate to push and to 'go with her body'. The doctor intervened and told Kate not to push as the hospital was in sight. She [the doctor] didn't want the baby born at the roadside. Kate found this hard and looked at me for guidance. I felt it appropriate to continue to tell Kate to do as she felt necessary and to push if she wanted to.

Kate: It didn't help that I was being given conflicting advice – don't push – push. I felt intense anger [often associated with transition]. Who was holding me? How long would I continue freefalling?

Pema was born in the hospital on 12th April 1995, a full term baby weighing 7lb 8oz. It was a vaginal birth with an episiotomy.

Kate: She was blue, she seemed big and strong. Cheophel told me that she looked dead and he burst into tears. I was just so relieved that she was out, and alive; that was it, we did it, the baby is born, end of struggle, I thought. I didn't realise that the struggle had only just begun.

Sheena: We arrived in hospital and Pema was born immediately. Her condition was poor and she went to the neonatal intensive care unit. This was the worst experience of my career. In bed that night I thought so much about Kate and Cheophel and their sadness and worry. I didn't sleep much and went through my actions, feeling sure that I had acted appropriately, although I remember wishing I had taken Kate in my car to hospital: an action warranting instant dismal.

Two supervisors of midwives scrutinised my records and called for me the following day. The meeting was unnerving due to its formality, but my seniors assured me that there were no discrepancies with my care and that my record keeping was good. I visited Kate twice that day, and became part of the grief and concern that enveloped the whole family. Sometimes I wondered if my colleagues felt blame towards me as some didn't really know the story. I also felt alienated by midwives who believed in a 100% hospital birth system, as they said nothing to me. Not much support really.

Kate: I remembered meeting the doctor the next day by chance on the corridor. She enquired after 'baby' and then said to me, 'So next time you will be having baby in hospital, yes?' I was too socked to reply, but felt like slapping her.

Kate and Pema came back to their borrowed home after three weeks in intensive care.

Kate: We had not been in contact with hospital social workers. We had not been offered any counselling. We came home with drugs for Pema and a telephone number for Scope given by one of the nurses. I remember thinking at the time 'Scope, that used to be the Spastics Society, why has he given me that?'

The words cerebral palsy had not yet been used in connection with my baby. She was so beautiful and precious, our first born child, nearly lost to us. But as she gradually came off the phenobarbitone, a sedative which had kept the seizures under control, she began to scream. She screamed round the clock. She could not be put down even for a second, without hyper-extending and screaming. She slept in five minute snatches and then only if she was being jogged about and bounced vigorously. Thus began a three year round-the-clock marathon. Our arms grew strong, but our spirits grew weak. We became exhausted. There was no let up, no involvement from social services, no respite care, no professional support apart from visits to the consultant for scans and checkups. More drugs were given to help Pema sleep. They were ineffective and that was when the epilepsy kicked in, leading to more drugs, prescribed by trial and error. Over the next year, no-one addressed the emotional side of what we had been through and continued to go through. We were expected to cope. Four lives could very easily have been lost at this point; Cheophel tried to take his life, I seriously considered aborting my second child, and then taking my own life; and there were times when we had to leave Pema alone screaming just to prevent ourselves from harming her. We were just so tired. We couldn't see a way forward. No-one knew how things were for us.

Sheena: My work location had changed, but I stayed in touch with Kate and her family. My desperation continued, seeing the distress and despair of this young family. What could I do? Eighteen months after Pema was born Kate had another baby.

Kate: There were medical reasons why I couldn't go for a homebirth this time, even though the system for transfer to hospital had changed. I requested permission for Sheena to be my midwife. I wanted to do it with her by my side again; I wanted it to be a shared experience which could help us both, and it was. I think it was at that point that I reconnected with my own inner strength.

Sheena: It was important for me to be asked by Kate to care for her when she was pregnant with her second child, and it gave me hope and confidence in myself as a midwife. Some two and half years after Pema's birth, Kate and her family were at a charity event for disabled children. A solicitor, who was a personal friend of Jane, the charity founder, was speaking at the event on the litigation process. After the talk, Jane introduced me to the solicitor, told him the bare bones of Pema's birth and suggested that he take a look at Pema's birth circumstances to see whether he felt that there was any negligence on the part of the NHS Trust.

Kate: I went along with it; I felt that it would be quite clear cut: either it would come out that they had messed up with the transfer to hospital, or it would be shown that everything was done properly. It seemed like a good idea to have someone 'independent' look at the facts. I was still very upset about things, used to burst into tears in shops, at meetings, whenever Pema was mentioned really. I suppose I was looking to the solicitor for a form of closure, and for support. But I was very naïve; I had no idea how litigation works, having no previous experience.

Sheena: Kate and Cheophel told me they had met a solicitor who was going to look into the birth of Pema. They respectfully asked me what I thought about this, and if I had any objections. They were clear they didn't want to hurt me, and that they were totally happy with the care I had given. Their concern was in relation to the doctor and the transfer to hospital. I felt unclear about the litigation process, and was naïve in my belief that, since I had given good and appropriate care to Kate and Pema to the best of my knowledge and ability, I had nothing to fear. I gave them my blessing and said I would do anything to help them.

After some years there was a change in the litigation process.

Kate: From the initial investigation the solicitor decided that there were strong grounds for a claim as there had been negligence during the transfer to hospital. This did not surprise me. I was asked to write an account of how I came to be giving birth at home and what happened just prior to labour, during labour and something of our life since then. It was very painful but I managed to detach myself from the process enough to write about it. Things took a long time, it was years before we received any reports from witnesses and expert witnesses. From the expert witness reports there were new allegations which focused on the care of the midwives, which we had never been worried about. We were told that the case would now have to include all these new findings. After the statement, which I sent in, I was not asked to give my comments on any of the reports that came in; I was told that as Pema's litigation friend I had a duty to accept the reports of experts I ordered to seek justice for her. My role in the process became very passive. It seemed to have a life of its own.

Sheena: The Trust's solicitor emailed me to ask me to call her immediately. There were new allegations, this time challenging my care. She would send the account, but told me not to worry. I read them with horror when they arrived. My first thought... did Kate believe this? I wasn't allowed to find out. Did she think I had cared for her inappropriately, without skill and judgement and that I had failed her? She signed to say she did. Oh God, this couldn't be true. I felt such anger towards the 'expert' midwife who wrote things about my care, that was good and provided with such passion.

The local press became involved. The story made front page news, detailing names and allegations against Sheena. Kate was out of the country and unaware of the events unfolding. The papers were local to the town where Sheena was born and lived most of her life, and where she worked as a community midwife.

Sheena: My colleague had bought the paper on her way into work on a late shift. She brought it straight to me. Horror. It couldn't really be happening. How can this be allowed when nothing was proven and no case heard? My name, my career, my reputation were on the line. What would the mothers for whom I have cared over the many years think? I felt sure they would think... 'lucky escape' or liken me to Harold Shipman. This may seem ludicrous and far removed from reality. But it was reality for me. Would I need to leave my job? My children had comments at school, my neighbours quietly mentioning it to my husband at the bottom of the garden. There were pointed fingers.

Kate: We returned from a very difficult but amazing trip to visit my husband's family in Tibet. He hadn't been back since leaving as a refugee 17 years earlier. I was pregnant with my fourth child. We were all ill and exhausted. We were fighting to get adaptations done in the home before my pregnancy advanced much further, so that I wouldn't have to lift Pema so much. We were waiting for a date for major hip surgery for Pema whose left hip was fully dislocated. She was in constant pain and spent much of the time screaming. And to top it all we were presented with the front page newspaper article. Everyone we knew assumed that we had consented to the article and that what we were doing was taking Sheena to court. Without any knowledge of the facts, everyone assumed we were wrong. A petition to the newspapers was circulating, saying that it was wrong to print these unproven accusations about Sheena. We agreed that it was wrong, but felt hurt that the petition didn't say that it was also wrong to portray us as enemies of Sheena. We were following a legitimate legal process but were being treated as if we were the wrongdoers not the victims. There were comments from mums at school and insults from people who had formerly supported us. There were accusations that we were money grabbers. We had support from no-one. Even close friends urged us to drop the case due to the damage it was doing to our family and to Sheena's. I felt deep depression for the next few months, isolation. I hated living in Clitheroe and wished for it all to be over. Our solicitor encouraged us to keep going and soon we would have the financial security to be able to move away.

But things didn't work out that way...

Kate: The solicitor had only met me one time after that initial meeting. Now he came to visit us with the barrister. I had made it clear that our concerns did not involve the midwives but rather the emergency services. They explained that although negligence had been firmly established with regard to the transfer to hospital, causation had not, because it was difficult to prove that the delays caused by the negligence were the cause of brain damage. The expert witnesses were saying that Pema could have been born sooner, if transfer had been more efficient, but probably not less than 1 hour after the bradycardia. They would be using all the evidence, including the evidence against the midwives, to support the case, and as Pema's litigation friend I had a duty to allow them to proceed. There had been an offer of a small out-of-court settlement, which was less than the amount that they would be paying in court costs, so no risk. The solicitor warned me that if we didn't go to court I would spend the rest of my life wondering what would have happened if we did. I had just had a baby, I was very open, quite emotional. I knew that I couldn't stand up in court and pretend that I believed the midwives had been to blame even if it was necessary to do so. I also knew that whatever part I played in the proceedings if the case was won on those grounds and not on the grounds of the mess up of the hospital transfer I would spend the rest of my life regretting it.

We telephoned the solicitor a few days later and asked to accept the out of court settlement and withdraw the case. The offer of a settlement was then withdrawn, and it had to go to appeal. Eventually we received an amount of money which has not changed Pema's life much, except that we could buy her a wheelchair adapted van. We still live in the same place, we can't afford to move. We still feel isolated, let down by the community, unsupported, outsiders. Pema the brave and the beautiful continues to be the epicentre of our lives.

Kate has her own perspective of how this system has failed her:

Kate: I believe in the right of a woman to birth in the place she feels is most appropriate for the type of birth experience she wants for her child and herself and the right to have unbiased information to make an informed choice, and support in the choice she makes. I believe that birthing can be an amazing spiritual experience. I believe that intervention should be available for emergencies but that it should not be the norm, and sensitivity is one of the greatest attributes of a good midwife – when to help, how to support, when to hold back, when to do nothing, letting woman and child lead the way. Pema's birth was such a shock; nothing in my life could have prepared me for that experience. But I think that the shock waves, which have coloured my whole life since then, could have been managed better, and I could have had support in integrating the experience, rather than being left with a huge open wound. I have lived with anger just below the surface for years now. There has been no real closure of the events of the day that Pema was born.

I had expected the litigation process to clear things up and allow me to find the type of resolution that no-one else had allowed. Apart from the legal system no-one was looking at Pema's birth at all, not even from the point of view of how it affected us as a family, or me as a woman. But the legal process made things less clear, muddied the waters and confused me even more. I still had no resolution or closure, just new issues to deal with. We were abandoned by the services that should have supported us. We were then taken on a desperate journey through the process of litigation, which promised a way to escape from some of the problems we had been left with, but which ultimately only added to our problems.

I feel that we should never have had to go through that process, and that justice is a game in which you have to play dirty if you want to win. We became pawns in that game, and it took a certain amount of moral courage to get out of it.

Although Sheena and I weren't allowed to communicate during the whole process I felt it important to send cards and letters to reassure her that there was no personal animosity, no change in my feelings for her. Why did we have to be placed on opposite sides of this artificial fence? Discussion of the case with Sheena since it was closed has been the only thing that has really helped me to face what happened and come to terms with it, and to start unravelling the threads of anger running through my life. I was not free to choose the place of birth for my third and fourth children, who were born without any intervention or medication, and could have been born at home. There were too many issues, and it was clear I was not going to get support. I wasn't going to do homebirth as a battle: I had other battles to fight on Pema's behalf.

I don't regret my decision to enter into the process of litigation; what happened at Pema's birth was swept under the carpet and litigation was the only choice on offer for me to face what happened so that I would be able to close that chapter. I do regret that there is no system in place in this country that can allow a family to honestly and openly request what happened in circumstances such as ours to be looked at, without the need for someone to blame. I regret that there isn't a supportive way to acknowledge events and their far-reaching consequences, even accept shortcomings, provide redress, and enable us all to get on with our lives, integrating the experience, however difficult. And while we struggle to support Pema, thousands of pounds of public funds have been spent, both on the side of the NHS and through legal aid provided to Pema, most of this going to solicitors. Would this money not have been better spent supporting the damaged child? I have no regrets about withdrawing from the court case; it was the only way for me to remain whole, and in my case I could see that the outcome would constitute neither justice nor clarification nor the closure I sought. I do very much regret that the key players here, Sheena, Sheena's family, myself, and my family, have had to go through so much heartache, and that my birth-damaged daughter does not have what she needs to make the best of her difficult life.

Sheena also has her perspective as a midwife about how the system failed her, and how it should change:

Sheena: I believe in a woman's ability to birth her baby, and that unbiased information should be offered to all women to help them choose their birth environment, with appropriate support for ultimate safety. Risks and benefits should include those in hospitals, as well as home. Pema's birth taught me that I can't always make things right, and sometimes, no-one can. It has, however, destroyed part of me that believed and respected British systems, and it has borne in me disgust in the purpose and philosophy of the press. I didn't know how to act appropriately following Pema's birth. Kate was too traumatised to discuss events in detail, and I was unsure of doing so. No discussions took place between senior medical teams or managers with Kate as to the sequence of events and how things could be better. This has now changed, and there would be a dialogue with Kate and her family, and potentially more support. Once the litigation process began, the destruction started, for me and for Kate. I wasn't allowed to communicate with her at all, which became harder following the press incidents. I wanted to speak to her and to tell her the allegations were false and that my care was good, but couldn't. Since the closure of the case we have discussed events at length. I feel betrayed by a system that wouldn't let me care for Kate when she had her third and fourth babies. I would have cared for her at home if Kate desired.

What changes should take place? Sheena and Kate feel:

Sheena: In midwives' training, students need to learn about the litigation processes and their effects, without the fear of blame.

Kate: Parents of damaged children need to know about what they could be letting themselves in for entering litigation, and perhaps a solicitor is not the best person to offer that advice.

Sheena: Health services need to continue to commit to transparency and openness within their services, and acknowledge failure with an apology if appropriate.

Kate: There needs to be acknowledgment of the events and their emotional impact, the questions that arise, even the ones with uncomfortable or no easy answer. Different aspects will need addressing at different times, but without open acknowledgment this can't happen. Litigation should not be the only way for this conversation to take place.

Sheena: Parents of babies born damaged or in need of long-term care should receive immediate support, without the need for blame.

Kate: The birth of a damaged child should not require parents to turn into fierce warriors continuously fighting for support and services. Litigation should not provide the only way for families to guarantee that their child's needs will be met.

Sheena: The media should be prohibited by law to publish details of health care professionals, unless they are a proven danger to the public. It seems that women are losing out in all of this, and that solicitors are the only ones to gain. And yet, due to our belief in each other and in spite of what has happened, we have travelled a full circle and are firmly back to together again, where we started.

Kate: I trust and respect Sheena as a midwife and friend and, given the right circumstances, I would have no hesitation in asking her to support me in delivering my baby at home. I would advise my own daughters that, given the right circumstances, home is the best place to bring your child into the world.

Sheena: I still believe in homebirth and recently supported my own daughter in her homebirth choice. My philosophy is clear that women must do as they feel, and be given unbiased evidence-based information to make their choice. Kate and her family are an important part of my life, and I will always feel privileged to be part of theirs.

So what next?

Kate and Sheena: We were almost destroyed by this experience, for very little gain, and although we are back together, the litigation system continues to drive women and midwives apart. In 2003, the Government consulted on a document entitled *Making Amends* (Department of Health, 2003), which set out proposals for reforming the approach to clinical negligence in the NHS. These 'redress' reforms however, have never been implemented.

In 2004/05 £422 million was paid out in litigation costs. An example of how costs can run so high is that Kate's case took almost 8 years to complete, and her solicitor charged £100 against the case every time a phone call was made to Kate. We feel that public money needs to be targeted where it is needed as opposed to lining the pockets of the legal profession. New Zealand, Scandinavian countries and France have introduced no fault schemes for medical injury and Virginia and Florida in America are introducing no fault compensation for babies with birth-related neurological injuries. The advantages of these systems include the fact that lawyers are not routinely involved, reducing the amount of costs to the legal profession and enabling more efficient targeting of resources.

Kate wanted to tell her story for clarity, to make sense of what happened, to assist in the integration of the experience. She feels it may promote a connection, with other women, midwives and mothers, to encourage them to have courage and to give insights into how the current system is failing. Sheena feels the same; by telling her story she wants to strengthen professional courage and belief in women and midwives as true partners.

Reference

Department of Health (2003) *Making Amends: A consultation paper setting out proposals for reforming the approach to clinical negligence in the NHS.* The Stationery Office, London

CHAPTER 6

Tales of healing

Gill's interview with Jeanette

For my doctoral research, I interviewed 14 women to explore their experiences of traumatic and subsequent positive childbirth events. Through listening to and reading their birth stories, I uncovered a heroic journey of childbirth and motherhood. This was a journey that transgressed through the devastation associated with a traumatic birth to women regaining courage, strength and determination to face a future birth event. The ending to their journey was an overwhelming sense of achievement and fulfilment of a healing, positive birth.

In this chapter, I present one woman's journey. When I met Jeanette, she was 37 years old, married and living with her husband and two children. Her eldest child (son) was aged 7 and her youngest child (daughter) was 16 months.

During her first pregnancy Jeanette attended hospital and National Childbirth Trust antenatal classes. She approached her birth with an open mind, and a willingness to be guided by expert opinion.

'I had been to parentcraft classes, antenatal classes at hospital and NCT, so I was well informed and pretty open-minded. My birth plan was very much – you're the experts and I'll be guided by your experience and judgements, but if possible I'd like this, this and this.'

On 7th November, 1998 Jeanette experienced a 'show' and the onset of frequent pain. Following a sleepless night she attended the delivery suite at the local hospital. She was examined by an unknown health professional and informed that she wasn't having proper contractions and wasn't in established labour yet and was 'bundled off home'. This pattern repeated itself over the next five days. Jeanette was unable to sleep due to the increasing severity of pain and physical complications (hot flushes and oedema of her feet and ankles). Her frequent attendance at the hospital was infiltrated by intrusive procedures (external and internal examinations) followed by invalidation of her claims of labour. Whenever Jeanette requested pain relief, the health professionals insisted on a vaginal examination being performed. As these examinations did not confirm the onset of labour, no pain relief was provided. This led to a repeated cycle of pain – promise of pain relief

– vaginal examination – no medication. Jeanette received an extensive number of vaginal examinations over the course of her labour.

'I felt like I was [in labour], you know I'd nothing to compare it to obviously as it was my first baby'

Jeanette described her interactions with health professionals as 'impersonal' due to 'not knowing anyone'. She felt de-personalised and even 'abused' through sensitive procedures being performed by relative strangers. Procedures were often undertaken with no explanations provided, and on occasion without her consent.

'What he actually did was sweep my membranes, but never told me what he was going to do, I had no idea and it was really, really painful... he didn't ask me if he could do it or explain what he was doing and that has stayed with me ever since really... it felt very intrusive and even abusive... I didn't know him.'

Jeanette had never been in receipt of medical or hospital procedures. Furthermore, her unending faith in the health professionals' 'expertise' led her to minimise and to doubt her physical as well as her intuitive bodily responses.

'I'd never been in hospital before, never been ill, never had an op or anything, so it was a big thing being in hospital [.....] and I felt like I was soft, you know, they were saying take a paracetamol, so I would go home, take a paracetamol and nothing would help.'

As time progressed, Jeanette's sense of helplessness and hopelessness magnified. She became 'lost' to the experience and process of childbirth through feeling isolated, desperate and out of her depth. Like other women I interviewed, Jeanette felt that at some point she was going to die during her labour. In Jeanette's case her demise would have been considered a relief due to the severity of pain, suffering and exhaustion she had endured.

'It was a relief and I thought, I'm dying and I thought, that's ok because it's got to be better than this.'

As a consequence, her positive anticipations and expectations of childbirth and motherhood were left far behind.

'The whole point of having a nice cuddly baby had been lost days before.'

On the 13th November, 1998, a caesarean section was performed and a 10lb 12oz male infant was delivered. During the operation the health professionals realised the baby had been 'stuck' in a posterior position. The size of her baby was only appreciated after the caesarean incision had been made too small, which subsequently caused her son to suffer shoulder dystocia. The labour and birth resulted in Jeanette experiencing innumerable physical, mental and emotional complications.

'I just felt like I was about 90 years old, I felt like I'd been run over by a truck [....] I remember thinking I'm brain damaged.... I could hardly speak, I was slurring my speech, I just literally couldn't function... from my breast bone down to my pubic bone was black and blue, it just looked like somebody had beaten me up.'

Jeanette held a 'scream inside of her' during her stay in hospital. On her return home, this negative energy emerged through post-traumatic stress responses through repeated and distressing flashbacks, nightmares and constant ruminations. Self-reprisals were held against herself and her husband for 'allowing' these events to have occurred.

'When I got home it hit me like a ton of bricks and I started having flashbacks... I think I should have screamed like Sunday or Monday and said, "I've had enough and don't leave me like this and the pain's too much," I never said I've had enough, I let them leave me, I blamed myself for a long time, blamed .... [husband] for not stepping in and saying you can't leave her like this.'

In the immediate and longer post-natal period Jeanette perceived herself as 'completely destroyed'. She felt 'unable to recognise herself' and that this experience had 'ruined my life'. On a physical level, the severity of trauma led to extended difficulties in general mobility and providing basic care for her son.

'It's like somebody breaks your legs and expects you to run a marathon.'

On an emotional level she had to 'fight' to create a positive relationship with her son. She experienced marital difficulties, social isolation, and was left with a shattered perception of the world.

'I'd gone from a really happy marriage and wanting this baby and a healthy pregnancy and being really excited to my world being absolutely shattered.'

To a significant extent, Jeanette's devastated self-perceptions were related to her sense of betrayal. She had trusted that the 'experts' would care for her, listen to her and treat her as a valuable member of society; the subsequent breach of her beliefs was a difficult lesson to comprehend.

'What I went through was unbelievable, I can't believe I put up with that for that length of time but it was because I trusted the people looking after me.'

When Jeanette's flashbacks and nightmares became uncontrollable, she eventually sought help by re-contacting her NCT tutor. The support that she received, as well as the exoneration of her self-perceived culpability created a crucial turning point for Jeanette.

'I suppose it was the first time that I actually articulated to somebody that I thought I was soft and she [NCT tutor] just looked at me and said, "Jeanette you're not soft, it wasn't your fault," and that made a big difference, just saying that and it encouraged me to get in touch with the hospital.'

Seven months after her son's birth, Jeanette, her husband and her mother attended an appointment with a consultant obstetrician. The purpose of the meeting was for Jeanette and her birth partners to obtain answers; however, the unexpected admission of blame that they received was overwhelming.

'I just wanted answers. So I went back and .... [consultant obstetrician] introduced herself and said, "I've spent the last few days going through your notes, I've gone through the whole week, your theatre notes as well, every detail and I just want you to know how sorry I am that this has happened to you," and I just burst into tears. I couldn't believe that someone had apologised to me and, yeah it was a mistake, it shouldn't have been like that.'

This apology was followed by in-depth discussions and explorations of Jeanette's labour and birth. She not only wanted to know what had happened, but more importantly why it had happened.

'I needed to understand it, because how could it go so badly wrong?'

Jeanette's recovery was prolonged and extensive. It included physiotherapy, hydrotherapy, dental treatment, counselling for post-traumatic stress, treatment for endometriosis as well as experiencing a miscarriage (and associated complications). The endometriosis and miscarriage resulted in numerous surgical operations being performed. Jeanette's repeated attendance at the operating theatre forced her to re-visit her fears and triggered flashbacks from her traumatic birth. The sights and sounds (such as the lift doors closing) of the hospital caused uncontrollable re-living of her birth experience.

'The operation floored me, I had to stay in overnight and my flashbacks started again and I was in the same recovery room and everything as when I had .... [her son] so it was another trigger and I just went right back into it. So it was really hard and it just became my life, trying to recover and get what I needed to recover... and it was emotional but it was also physical.'

It was through the counselling that Jeanette recognised that in order to cope with motherhood, she had dissociated the experience of birth from the experience of having her son. It took two years of support before Jeanette felt 'safe' and 'strong' enough to 'piece' the experiences together.

'I brought the whole process together, I pieced it together in my own mind, but it had to be safe, I had to be strong enough to do that and to feel safe enough to do it.'

Some five years after her son's birth Jeanette became pregnant again. She requested an elective caesarean and was allocated under the care of the consultant obstetrician. The obstetrician provided her debriefing, co-ordinated her care during her endometriosis and miscarriage as well as offered additional support and care for Jeanette and her birth partners. Without this support, Jeanette believes she would never have had a further child: 'I really believe that without .... [obstetrician] I wouldn't have a daughter. She, in particular, got me through and made the difference.'

Jeanette received antenatal support, advice, information and care from a range of clinical professionals. These professionals were an essential life-line to guide her through the increasing fear and anxiety of the forthcoming birth.

'When I was talking to .... [consultant midwife] when I was expecting, and she said, "What do you need, what will help?" My analogy is that I'm in this hot air balloon and it's going to float away with me in it but I need certain key people to be holding onto the ropes on the ground to stop me from floating away [...] I can remember that was the risk I took having another baby, that I would disappear and this time I wouldn't come back and that was real to me.'

Her regular antenatal appointments and check-ups encompassed clinical as well as emotional support. Visits to the delivery suite and operating theatre were also undertaken for Jeanette to address her negative flashbacks associated with the birth environment. However, the experience of trauma, and the despair of a miscarriage meant that neither Jeanette nor her husband could relax and look forward to what was ahead.

'This pregnancy was totally different because there was anxiety, and you can't really get excited and enjoy it, you just want it to last and I thought if I can go nine months with this pregnancy, can I have a normal healthy baby at the end of it and can I be normal and healthy at the end of it as well? It was such a massive risk.'

Jeanette was provided with 24-hour contact numbers, as well as the work patterns of her birth team. Through consultations with all key professionals, and detailed birth plans being formed, Jeanette and her birth partners knew 'exactly' what was, or what could occur during the birth. The extensive and individualised support she received eventually led to meaningful and trusting relationships being forged.

'They earned my trust after I had felt so badly let down, I felt that they wanted me to trust them and wanted to prove me wrong... they went the extra mile for me.'

Jeanette approached her subsequent birth with the belief that her birth 'really mattered' to her caregivers, and there was 'nothing else' that anyone could do to ensure a positive outcome.

When the planned caesarean section was performed, Jeanette felt 'in control', 'cared for' and 'safe'. Her sense of control was related to her active engagement in the birth; as well as the mutual reciprocal relationship with her caregivers, based on trust, value, concern and respect.

The outcome of Jeanette's second birth culminated in far more than a healthy baby.

'I can remember when they were in theatre, ... [obstetrician] lifting .... [daughter] up and I can remember it for the rest of my life and just thinking, it just made me complete, just seeing her.'

Jeanette was euphoric following this birth. The overwhelming sense of 'love' she had for her daughter left her feeling 'fantastic', 'amazing' and that she had experienced 'a miracle'. Jeanette had believed that her son's birth was a miracle because they had both survived. The miracle of her positive birth was a peak experience of joy and happiness. While reassurance of a 'different' birth had been promised antenatally, this was never truly believed until after her second birth had been performed. The trauma rather than the type of birth signalling the vital difference in her birth experiences.

While Jeanette's post-operative recovery was uncomplicated, her daughter went on to experience difficulties (she was lactose intolerant). However, the physical and emotional well-being created through a 'joyful' birth meant that Jeanette was 'starting from the right foot' in providing maternal care.

Through overcoming defeat by 'facing fears'; engaging in 'battle' to access the care that was needed; and the support received via trusted professionals, Jeanette and her husband achieved the 'perfect happy ending' of a positive birth event. Jeanette used an analogy of a 'broken jigsaw' to describe the aftermath of trauma. A positive birth pieced the 'picture back together' through her feeling 'whole again'.

While this positive birth was a happy and joyous affair, it resurrected and magnified what had been 'lost' through trauma.

'I can remember such a high [...] and then having a flashback to how I felt looking at .... [son] in his little cot at the side of my bed, thinking, "Oh my God, that must have affected how I looked after him," because I was like two different people.'

As Jeanette's conceptions of the world were shattered through trauma, it has been impossible to revert to her a priori perceptions. Her birth trauma was so destructive and fundamental that it has 'changed me forever'.

'I'm lucky because I think my journey's complete because I've got .... [daughter], and its just the happiest ending ever, but it's the worst part of my life, I've faced the toughest things I'll ever have to face getting there and it has changed me forever.'

Despite her altered reality of the world, a further baby provided Jeanette with a sense of relief that her family was 'complete'. An experience of joy also provided added meanings as it meant that her reproductive choices were dependent on personal values (such as financial constraints) as opposed to fear. The 'blessing' of a healing birth provided the 'closure' that she needed to move on with her life.

'To have gone through this and to feel finally that I'm coming out the other side is such a relief and I feel a lot more free from the worry, the not knowing and the fears. To not have that in my life any more is fantastic and to have a positive result, two healthy children and just be so content.'

A healing birth represented a redemptive experience for Jeanette. It enabled her to 'forgive' and resolve the dysphoria and distress associated with trauma, as well as to create more meaningful and positive self-perceptions of childbirth and motherhood. It represented an experience that not only changed her future, but also changed her past.

'I knew that having another baby would change the future but I didn't realise it was possible to change the past, and it did, it just was the ultimate healing process.'

Lynda's story

This birth story arguably started seven years and two births prior to this one. My first experience of childbirth was, on reflection, unpleasant. Traumatic almost seems an overdramatic term to use, however, looking at how it affected me at the time and since, it may be the most appropriate word.

Seven years ago, after an uneventful pregnancy, I started in labour. Having no idea of how my body would labour and with the comments of my mother that 'I didn't really labour, just felt some pains and you were here,' I contacted the hospital very early on.

I listened to the advice, took two paracetamol and had a bath. My contractions then were coming every 15 minutes so I decided to go to hospital.

I was taken down to the delivery suite from the antenatal ward in a wheelchair (although I had previously been mobilising well), allocated a very small room and was asked to get on the bed. Except for a few trips to the toilet I remained semi-recumbent for the remainder of my labour. My labour slowed down from this point onwards although I got to full dilation approximately six hours later. There then followed a series of interventions: my waters were broken, I was started on syntocinon and everything seemed to get more painful. I went from coping with my TENS machine, to using entonox then pethidine, to requesting an epidural. My desire for a drug-free birth had long passed.

I ended up having to have a forceps delivery. I am only aware of most of what happened during my labour thanks to having read my notes retrospectively. What I do remember though, seven years later, was the sense of almost being violated. I remember the focus being purely on my vagina; I was put into stirrups and there appeared to be an influx of people between my legs. I know I was cut and conversations were had over me about what was happening – the baby's heartbeat was falling and taking a time to recover. Looking back I felt like a vessel and almost incidental in the birth of my daughter. I wanted to close my legs, I wanted to return to my pregnant state, I wanted to regain my dignity, I wanted to be in control again.

Postnatally, I needed to have my episiotomy refashioned and this, coupled with my experience, put a definite strain on the physical side of my relationship with my husband. With regard to my daughter, if I am brutally honest, I seemed to switch from feelings of guilt that I hadn't been able to deliver her properly, to ones of resentment that her birth had resulted in this experience. The guilt was compounded by the comments of a midwife on the postnatal ward who told me that my baby was crying so much because I had let her be passed round by the grandparents that afternoon during visiting time when she must have a bad headache due to being a forceps delivery. I was actually grateful to the midwife when she offered to take her for a while to let me sleep. When she returned her to me she told me that she had given her some Calpol and a bottle which she 'gulped down'. This upset me as I was breastfeeding and, though I know it is irrational, I felt like I was starving her too on top of everything else I had put her through.

This is difficult to admit, but I know I found it hard to bond with her and this created more feelings of guilt. All this culminated in me suffering from postnatal depression. When I discovered I was pregnant again just over a year later I was concerned that it may happen again.

My next pregnancy was not as smooth, and I ended up with gestational diabetes. Unfortunately, this was not discovered until late on in my pregnancy by which point the baby seemed to be on the big side. I was scanned and offered an elective caesarean by the consultant, based on the baby's size and my previous delivery. I was unsure and discussed it with my husband. He made the comment that he, 'Wouldn't want us to go through that again,' and it was at this point that I realised that our daughter's birth had not just affected me. He was a lot more aware of what was happening at the time than I was and when my daughter was taken from the room immediately following her delivery to be 'checked' he was the one left worrying. I think at this point I had retreated into myself and hadn't been as conscious of what was occurring.

It may sound odd considering that I was having a caesarean but during my second experience of childbirth I felt much more in control. I was kept fully informed of what was happening and had a great midwife who I had got to know antenatally. I felt a part of the process, and although I am aware that things are different with a second child, I had no bonding issues and, thankfully, apart from mild 'baby blues', did not experience any depression. It was partly due to the midwife I had at this birth. Seeing the difference a caring midwife could make, I decided to look into midwifery as a career.

I became pregnant during the second year of my midwifery course. Being a student midwife gave me a different perspective, and the more I learned and saw the more I felt that my first birth could have been so different.

We decided not to tell the children or anyone else until after the 20 week scan, so in a way it didn't seem real until that time. When people knew, the realism that I would be going through childbirth again hit me. I really did not want to return to where I had had my first child and, mixed with shift work and hormones, it all came to a head and I broke down at work one day. My mentor suggested I contacted the consultant midwife at the hospital I was working in to see about changing my booking from my home town.

And so started my first contact with caseload midwifery. The consultant midwife obtained my notes and made time for us to go through them. I cannot describe what a difference this made to me. I was able to see that my body hadn't failed me. I had got to full dilation, in spite of the situation, and forceps were required due to my fatigue, not inability. It wasn't an exercise in blame, rather we could see what had gone wrong and how it could be different this time. I was very motivated after the meeting and felt I was capable of having a normal birth. My only concern was that there were surely people in a greater need of this service than I was, and comparatively, my births were not that traumatic; my children were well and thriving and so was I. The consultant midwife explained that my reaction to recounting the birth should indicate to me how traumatic I had found it and trauma is an individual thing.

It is difficult to describe the difference that having one-to-one care from such a caring and proficient midwife made. She was part counsellor (my sister had lost a baby at 38 weeks just six months prior to my falling pregnant), allowing me time to talk through all my fears; part information-provider as I wanted to, ideally, have a water vaginal birth, so I needed to know the risks and benefits; and, due to this, also my 'mouthpiece' when talking with my consultant.

As we built the relationship antenatally I had confidence in her and she gave me immense confidence that I could achieve the birth I wanted. And here is where I finally understood the meaning of the term empowerment. It appears in many textbooks and guidelines and I thought I had an understanding of its meaning but now I truly did. Although a proponent of normality, I felt that I could have the birth I wanted. For instance, if I had decided that I was worried about the baby's size or its non-arrival (incidentally 9lb 12oz and 42 + 1 week) and really wanted a caesarean I truly believe she would have done everything she could to ensure I could have one. That is not to say that she wouldn't have discussed with me the reasons behind my decision, but ultimately I trusted her to listen to me and help me attain my wishes. Undeniably, it was this trust that resulted in me not going down that route, as I felt safe in the knowledge that no door had been shut to me. The same goes for pain relief. I wanted a drug-free birth, but again I knew that in labour, if I had insisted on an epidural, I would have been able to have one. I was empowered to have my birth of choice because I knew there was someone with me who would support me in any choice I made.

After a long wait the birth itself was at a faster pace. Due to the risk of induction for vaginal births after caesarean sections we held off for as long as possible, although there was also the risk of the baby getting too big.

After two membrane sweeps and a few false starts I was admitted onto the delivery suite to have my waters broken. This happened around 9.45am on a Thursday morning and by 10.30am I was contracting regularly every three minutes and mobilising well. The fact that I had already formed a relationship with my midwife gave me the freedom to do and act as I wished without the worry of how she would feel. This was very freeing at this point because I felt annoyed and unsociable and did not want anyone to touch me, and preferably not speak to me!

I was finding it hard to cope with just my TENS machine, and decided to have some entonox at around 11.30am. I also had some monitoring at this time to check the baby was fine. This had been requested by the consultant as I had had a previous section. Then the pool was filled and I had an examination to assess my dilation at 12.00pm, as we had discussed the possibility of labour slowing up if I got in the water too early. I was found to be 4cm but still wished to get in the pool and understood what we would do if labour did slow down. That was not to happen though. I got in the pool at 12.45pm and suddenly everything seemed to speed up. My contractions were coming one after another and I did not seem to be getting any break and the thought crossed my mind whether I could be bothered getting out of the pool to get on the bed for an epidural. My midwife talked me through each contraction and I put any thoughts of getting out to the back of my mind, safe in the knowledge that if I wanted to, I knew I could. There then seemed to be a short respite and my midwife stepped out at about 1.20pm to take a phone call. Shortly after she had gone I felt pressure below during a contraction. I waited until the next one then felt amazed that my body seemed to be acting on its own accord. Between contractions I grunted at my husband to push the call button and upon her quick return vertex was visible. This was at about 1.30pm, 45 minutes after I had got in the pool. The water was fantastic – I had the freedom to move and felt weightless. A few contractions later and my baby's head was born, followed shortly by his shoulders at 1.44pm. I delivered the placenta on the bed while giving my son his first breastfeed.

I cannot put into words the difference the consultant midwife and my midwife made to my birth experience and also, perhaps surprisingly, the difference it has made to my thoughts on my first birth. It has been incredibly cathartic. I feel I have forgiven myself for what happened and accept that it is in the past and it need not affect me any more. Had I not had this experience

I think I would always have wondered what childbirth could be like. Now I know it can be wonderful and I remember on her final visit postnatally, my midwife asking me whether I had 'come down' from the whole thing yet; I hadn't. And now, nine months later I am still impressed with myself.

CHAPTER 7

Tales of triumph: A mother and a father's story

Liz's story

Finding out we were pregnant with our first child was a joy as we had been trying for several months without success. Pete and I were both excited and nervous at the thought of being parents but did not really know much about giving birth. Despite the antenatal classes, looking back, we were totally unprepared for what was to happen. We did not know how to help ourselves or get the best care from the midwives, as we did not know enough to be able to question decisions that were made, or feel confident enough to challenge or try to take control of the birth of our baby boy.

Despite the fact that on paper I had a textbook delivery, the labour and birth were traumatic and I could, for many years, only liken the shock I felt to being in a horrendous car accident which left me upset, depressed and emotionally detached from my baby.

On the antenatal ward I was ignored despite being in a lot of pain. I had to demand that my husband be allowed to come to the hospital as I felt that something was happening, but that nobody was listening to me. We were placed in a side room following a painful examination after which I was told nothing was happening and to try and get some sleep. Nobody came to check on me for another five hours, despite my being in agony, by which time I was 8cm dilated. I was told to get onto a wheelchair and was rushed up to delivery suite were I was told to start pushing and deliver my baby without any pain relief. I found delivering my baby a barbaric experience; something to try to forget, not cherish or remember.

I held our baby for the obligatory photographs then quickly told Pete that I didn't want to hold him any more. I certainly couldn't believe that I was expected to look after my baby when I felt like I had nearly died delivering him and had been awake for the last 36 hours and was absolutely exhausted. After being told to get into a bath, and being transferred to the postnatal ward, the midwives told us that it was time for my husband to leave as visiting was over. I felt so scared and alone, and found it astonishing that my husband was being told to leave as Max was both our baby. Pete was there for the delivery and now he couldn't stay with me, and at that time I needed his love and support more than ever. I spent the next three days in hospital, having flashbacks of the birth, not sleeping or eating properly, missing my husband and just wanting to be at home.

Once I was home I felt very low in mood and it seemed to take forever to heal post delivery. I was starting to feel depressed. When the health visitor came, I lied on the postnatal depression check because, as a nurse, I felt that people would expect me to be coping with everything. It wasn't until 18 months later when the panic attacks started that I knew I had to get some help from the GP.

On reflection I loved Max from the start because he was my baby and eventually the bond with him grew and I fell in love with him, but I did feel regret and guilt for a long time that he did not have a better start into this world. I blamed myself for not taking control of his birth and the midwives for not listening to me or helping me. I have never felt that Max was to blame for my feelings surrounding his birth, but I couldn't deal with my own trauma, feeling that I had already failed him as a mother at birth before I had even spent any time with him. I was made to feel needy and foolish in asking for help and for not having coped with his delivery.

The decision to get pregnant and have a second child was therefore very difficult knowing what had happened previously and, still taking medication for anxiety, it was difficult to see this pregnancy and subsequent birth being any different than before. So could I really put myself through all that again, especially as things seemed finally to be settling down? The anxiety and panic attacks were now few and far between, but Max was getting older and it felt like the timing was right to have another child so that the age gap was not too great between them. It had still taken me three years to be able to even consider having another baby.

When I found out I was pregnant, I was over the moon. I stopped taking the anxiety medication and for 6 months I felt great, happy to be pregnant and excited about meeting my baby, but then it suddenly hit me that I had to deliver this baby. I felt overwhelmed that I wouldn't be able to manage it, that I was going to at least need an epidural or a caesarean section. All I knew was that I couldn't go through that pain again feeling so out of control, being told what I could or couldn't do, and the thought of spending any time in hospital in pain was too much to bear. The thought that I might feel down after delivering my next child and not bonding with her was also playing on my mind. I broke down one day at the antenatal clinic and luckily a very understanding midwife recognised that I was going to need a lot more support than just the normal antenatal care and referred me to the caseload team. Within a week Jill Cooper phoned me at home to tell me that she had room on her caseload, that I would now get one-to-one home visits and, most importantly, that she would look after me throughout my pregnancy.

On Jill's first visit she listened to me and let me tell her all about what had happened last time, how I felt about it and what my fears were this time. I confessed to her that if I didn't get the birth right this time that I felt I wouldn't come out the other side of it with my mental health intact and this was my biggest fear.

I found Jill to be completely understanding of my feelings and supportive of my thoughts and needs for this pregnancy and delivery. Given my anxieties about returning to the hospital to give birth Jill talked to me about homebirth as an option and also looking into using a birthing pool if that was what I wanted to do.

It was a friend of mine who was a midwife who suggested that I research birth and read as much as I could in order to find out myself what sort of birth it was that I really wanted. Initially I had started reading Grantly Dick-Read's book *Childbirth Without Fear*, a hypno-birthing book, and then Janet Balaskas' *Active Birth* book in which she talks briefly about waterbirths and how relaxing they can be. I then bought Janet Balaskas' *Waterbirth* book which gave all the details and birth stories of waterbirths. Eventually I found what I wanted, although my initial reaction to homebirth was that I really wasn't sure about the safety aspect and how I would cope with the pain of childbirth at home.

However, after researching homebirth and waterbirths I decided that being at home could greatly reduce my anxiety, as being in hospital was one of my biggest fears. I knew that if I could reduce my anxiety then I would change my perception of the pain to be positive and life-affirming rather than being fearful of it and I would be able to tolerate the pain a lot better. I knew that I wanted to reduce my pain but without medical intervention, therefore having a waterbirth seemed like a good option and I felt that using a birthing pool would be very relaxing and help me get through labour calmly and also reduce my anxiety. Jill assured me that both mine and the baby's safety would be paramount throughout and she was very supportive of my decision of a home waterbirth.

Throughout my pregnancy. when I felt that I might change my mind. Jill constantly reassured me that I was in control of my labour and birth and that this was my decision. If I changed my mind and wanted to go to hospital to have my baby that this was fine too. I was in control of what was happening to me and Jill gently guided me through the process.

Jill also told me of a waterbirth website which also had lots of birth stories, and Jill herself gave me some birth stories from ladies who the team had looked after. As much as the birth stories helped me to see the positive feelings to be gained after giving birth, no one had had the same experience as me first time round and then gone on to have a positive experience next time, so I still remained anxious.

As my due date was getting nearer I felt myself becoming increasingly anxious about giving birth. Even though I had a well-thought-out birth plan I wasn't sleeping or eating properly and was very weepy. I told Jill how I felt and she asked me if I had ever considered homeopathy as an alternative therapy to helping reduce my anxiety. Homeopathy was something which I was very open to and, at the initial meeting with the homeopath, we talked for two and half hours about my feelings. It was a good outlet and it gave me the opportunity to talk to someone completely independent. Afterwards the homeopath gave me remedies which greatly reduced my anxiety and helped me to sleep. She showed me breathing and visualisation techniques and wrote affirmations for me, which I used throughout the pregnancy to keep me positive and focused. I visited her every week for the last four weeks of the pregnancy, and she was always available for advice over the phone when I needed it. I also bought a homeopathy kit for use during and after labour and birth and she advised me on which were the best remedies for me to use. It proved very useful.

For days before the birth I felt very up and down, excited about having the baby and then disappointed that I hadn't gone into labour, but then it happened. I was two weeks overdue, and there had been talk of inducing me, which I was very keen to avoid as the thought of being in hospital was too much. On Friday the 18th July at 10pm I started having contractions every 15 minutes. At first I tried to ignore them and get some sleep as I thought that the birth could be several hours away and I would need my energy later. After four hours, at 2am, I sent a text to Jill to say I thought I was in labour and she sent me a text me back telling me to relax but that she would come over if I wanted her to. At that time I didn't feel it necessary for Jill to come over, but by 4am the contractions were every 10 minutes and very strong. As labour started I used a homeopathic remedy to try and settle my anxiety which worked for a short period. I woke Pete up, he put the TENS machine on me and set up the birthing pool. By 5am Jill arrived, I was 4cm dilated and panic had set in. The TENS machine was only mildly effective and I was crying, saying that I just wanted to be pain free. I didn't want to get in the pool but I didn't want to leave the house and go to hospital, I was very confused.

Thankfully Jill encouraged me to at least try the pool and when I did it was absolute bliss. Although I could still feel the contractions, the pain had dramatically reduced and I felt like I could relax totally in the water during each contraction. The time I spent in the pool was so relaxing it felt like my own safe haven, and when the really strong contractions started I felt like I could close my eyes, float in the water and drift off into my own world. I was able to shut out the noise of the room and concentrate on getting through the contractions by relaxing and breathing. I was lucid throughout this labour, able to laugh, joke and hold conversations between contractions. This was a great relief and enabled me to connect with my husband, Jill and Anita, thereby preventing the overwhelming feeling of being alone which I had felt during my first delivery. In the water I found I could move myself into positions a lot more freely, using the sides of the pool for support and when things got really tough during labour and I felt I couldn't carry on, I used homeopathic remedies from my kit. These made me feel more positive when I felt I wouldn't be able to deliver my baby. Pete was also able to get close to me, sitting at the edge of the pool, and when I was ready to give birth he leant over the side holding my hands.

Having him so close also enabled me to get through the contractions as he made me feel that everything was all right and just to keep going as our baby would be here soon. I did get to a point where I needed the gas and air, which at the time made me feel I was cheating as I had come this far with just relaxing and breathing, but when I did get the gas and air I found I could totally relax through the strongest contractions and it was a very effective pain relief while I was pushing and delivering Lucy.

Jill was very supportive and encouraging throughout, she worked tirelessly during my labour ensuring that I and the baby were both well and I felt safe in her care allowing me to get on with labouring without fear. Not once did I ever feel frightened about not being at the hospital. I think this was because of Jill and Anita's great care, that I always felt that mine and my baby's health were always being considered.

The labour turned out to be a lot longer than with my first child, but this was the pace that my body needed to go at and when I felt exhausted Pete was ready with the homeopathic remedies to keep me going, as well as giving me lots of toast to keep my energy up. Using gas and air for the last hour and a half, eventually Lucy was born at 15.49pm with the help of Jill and Anita. I was so excited when I delivered her I couldn't believe that she had finally arrived. I was shouting, 'I did it, I can't believe I did it.' It was so joyful, Pete and I both cried. It was an overwhelmingly positive experience and a complete contrast from the delivery of my little boy.

After getting cleaned up and feeding Lucy I snuggled into bed with her and the day after I was full of energy, still beaming from delivering her. My recovery after giving birth was very quick, which I believe was due to the wonderful care I received and the fact that I had a homebirth, which allowed me to stay in my own familiar surroundings, eat and drink what I wanted, stay with my husband and little boy and get as much rest as I wanted in my own bed at home, without having to conform to strict hospital regimes and interventions. All these things helped me enjoy being with Lucy immediately. Within two weeks I was back to normal, attending children's parties with my little boy and Lucy and having family days out to the beach; a stark contrast to how I felt post-delivery after my first birth. I attribute all my positive feelings to the excellent care I had received during pregnancy, labour and birth. After Max's birth I could never understand women who said that as soon as their babies were born all the pain disappeared and was forgotten, as for a long time the birth was all I could think about. However, after having Lucy I felt exactly the same as all those women; the pain of the birth was the furthest thing from my mind, I only felt immensely proud to have delivered my baby at home and was totally in love with and amazed by this new little being.

I felt empowered during this pregnancy, labour and birth as I knew I had the support of a very caring midwife who told me that I was in control of what happened to me and my body. I knew that I had researched deeply the sort of birth that I wanted. I had hired the TENS machine, bought the birthing ball, aromatherapy oils and the birthing pool, and had consulted a homeopath to get remedies to help me. This had laid all the foundation stones for the birth I wanted. I had put everything in place to help myself this time round and taking an active role in the birth gave me this feeling of empowerment. Even if there were hard times during pregnancy and labour when I felt I couldn't do it, when I did do it I felt even more proud of myself. This time I had made this happen for me. If I hadn't taken control of my birth and been referred to the caseload team then I would have ended up in hospital having my baby and would have been left feeling completely dissatisfied and, at worst, traumatised again.

I know that Pete was a lot happier with a homebirth. Having all the equipment to hand that we needed in our own home and it being ours also helped Pete to feel empowered as a husband and a Dad as he had an active role to play in labour and delivery. He set up the TENS machine and it was his responsibility to set up, fill and then continually refill the birthing pool ensuring that I was kept warm. He also made lots of tea and toast for me, Jill and Anita. The girls felt he had done a great job and, as he was happy and relaxed, so was I.

On reflection I now know that what happened with Max's birth was completely avoidable and should never have happened. Women should be listened to even if they are incorrect in thinking that they are in labour. Their anxieties should not be ignored and they shouldn't be made to feel needy or foolish in asking for help. I now understand that I was and am a good mother to Max that it was the circumstances of his birth that mortified me, not the act of giving birth to him. I had carried him, loved him and cared for him for nine months inside me and I was made to fall at the final hurdle by others and I had to live with the consequences. But I have turned my fears into a positive experience and now, like other women, I too have a great birth story to tell of which I am very proud. This is my story now, it's my turn to let people know that I understand how bad things can be, but I've come out the other side of it totally unscathed and 100 times a better person following this pregnancy and Lucy's birth. I truly believe that if I can come through it that anyone can, no matter how bad the previous experience was. The key is having the right support, bond and trusting relationship with the midwife. I only knew Jill from the 32nd week of my pregnancy, but the bond we formed in that short time was so powerful it saw us through the good and the bad times resulting in a fantastic experience which I couldn't have done without her.

The care that Jill gave after Lucy's birth was also truly amazing. I cannot praise Jill's work highly enough. Without the relationship of trust that we had formed I know that Lucy's birth would not have been the positive experience that it was. Jill's dedication and commitment to me and my family has been wonderful and has changed my life, giving me the opportunity to believe in myself as a mother knowing that I can labour and deliver my baby.

Pete's story

I'd always wanted a baby but ideally two, a boy and a girl. After quite a stressful time trying for a baby I was overjoyed when I found out Liz was pregnant with our first.

However, nothing could prepare me for the next few years. I always saw myself as being aware of things happening in my life and having some sense of knowing what to do and when, but during the pregnancy the everyday stresses of life and not knowing exactly what Liz was thinking and going through meant that it took its toll on both of us. I felt helpless for most of the pregnancy and seemingly unable to help Liz when she needed support the most. I put this down mostly to a total lack of information about pregnancy and birth. However, not knowing that a whole wealth of information could have been provided by the hospitals and midwives, I felt completely isolated from any advice to help me support Liz. When Liz's waters broke we were both pretty calm, we packed according to plan and attended the hospital, excited and looking forward to the birth.

However, this soon changed as it became clear that labour was not imminent. The first midwife to see us was not helpful and if anything was obstructive and seemed oblivious to the fact I was even there. She then conducted a membrane sweep on Liz, but gave no explanation of what she was doing or why. She then left and we were ushered into a side ward not knowing what was happening. We assumed this was normal procedure. Shortly after I was uncompromisingly told to leave and was left feeling upset, deflated and unable to support Liz when she needed me most. At home I felt terrible, not knowing what was happening and unable to be there for my wife. Twenty four hours later I got a call from the hospital saying that my wife really needed me there and it became obvious that she had had to fight to get them to call me. Once there Liz and I were both relieved to be with each other again at this important time. This feeling was short-lived, however, as I was again asked to leave Liz and sleep in the day room at the other end of the ward. I begged to be allowed to stay in the room with her and I was begrudgingly told I could. I had to sleep on the hospital floor with my wife's bag for a pillow. No blanket or pillows were offered.

As the hours passed Liz needed pain relief and attention but the midwives were not interested. Despite being the early hours and relatively quiet, it was obvious the staff resented me being there. After several hours of comforting Liz and getting frustrated with the midwives' lack of enthusiasm for anything Liz was examined and found to be 8cm dilated and rushed to the delivery suite. I quickly got my head together and hope that I did the best I could for Liz and was so happy to become the father of a baby boy.

My anger and frustration went as I realised Liz needed me more than ever. The next few days, having to go home and visit Liz in hospital and arrange everything for her and my new son was exhausting, and I became upset that Liz and my son were still in hospital and I was at home. However, on having them both home I quickly became used to what was needed and became as involved as I could with everything. What I hadn't accounted for was how significantly this birth experience had affected Liz. The next year or two were very testing for us both and it is only now I realise what was going on. I was completely unaware of the depth of upset and emotional stresses Liz had gone through and endless arguments ensued with me failing to understand anything that was being said. I strongly believe that more information and care from the midwifery team could have avoided a whole host of problems. It was a hard lesson to learn and I sincerely hope other parents are more lucky with their birth experiences.

The decision to have a second child was made. However, after conceiving, it was quickly becoming obvious that the birth of our first child and the issues surrounding it were affecting Liz and she was becoming more and more anxious as the months went on. Out of nowhere came the welcome relief that Liz was to be put under the care of the caseload team. Jill Cooper, the midwife who came to visit us at home was just what Liz needed. Nothing was too much trouble and although my main concern was for Liz's welfare, I was anxious to get as involved as I could and Jill went out of her way to involve me. I was able to attend a series of follow up home visits, and any fears were alleviated. It was suggested that Liz should visit a homeopath. Although I was sceptical about the benefits of this, it benefited Liz and that was the most important thing.

When contractions started in the early hours, it was a calm affair and, as promised, Jill and her colleague attended at the appropriate time. A homebirth had been agreed and deep down I knew it would be the best option for Liz. Throughout the labour I was told everything that was happening and between us Jill and I were able to keep Liz calm and focused. Despite being the only one who never seemed to get any of the tea and toast that I made for hours on end it was a fantastic experience which I would recommend to any father to be. A long and smooth home waterbirth occurred and I now have the girl I always wanted. The difference in the two births is vast. I still cannot believe how awful the experience was that we went through with our first birth and that the lack of care could destroy what should have been the happiest time of our lives, or, more positively, how much difference the attitude of one midwife and the information and support received can make to a birth. However, we have got through everything stronger and happier than ever before and, as with most parents, we just get on with what life throws at us and cherish every moment with our children.

One of the best things that Jill encouraged us to do was to take photographs, some are of me during labour, looking very relaxed, and then some of me and Lucy immediately after her delivery. It is really satisfying to be able to look back at photographs of such a special event and know that those moments have been captured forever.

CHAPTER 8

Tales of midwives and obstetricians

Liz's story (Midwife)

Birth in regional Queensland Australia was something I had no knowledge of 10 years ago. As a midwife working in fairly progressive urban areas in both Australia and England I had never really thought much about not being able to have what I was used to – a variety of ways of providing and receiving care, until my husband decided that we should move to his home town. I visited and looked around this small and beautiful city and thought it looked great. It wasn't until I went to visit a naturopath a few weeks later and told her that I was a midwife that I had any concerns.

'The doctors run proper midwives out of town here,' I was told.

I still wasn't too worried, I was having a bit of 'down time' from midwifery as we had just relocated from the UK and thought, 'Well they haven't met me yet.'

However, it was soon to become a major issue. I was pregnant. This was my first pregnancy and it was very problematic. I can remember crying at night, telling my poor husband that I had always imagined being surrounded by the tender care of midwives during this time, having the care that I had imagined throughout my whole career. Instead I ended up with every array of obstetric ministration that you could think of during my first birth and I suffered badly afterwards as a result.

I decided I had better re-enter the workforce to see what I could do. I found the situation confronting me quite tragic. For the most part the midwives were unable to practise 'effectively' or really at all. I realised my work was cut out for me. Baby number two followed very quickly and was marginally better in that I knew at least what I was up against, but he had a heart defect and we 'needed' hospital care for him.... so on it went. I felt so deflated.

Somewhere after that birth I decided that, although I had worked inside the system as a midwife, with continuity at the centre of my practice for my whole career, I was going to have to break out. I set up in private practice and held my breath, waiting to be run out of town. I was very quiet about what I was doing. I didn't make a fuss initially and made a really big deal of supporting women in hospital, providing them with advocacy but acting very diplomatically while doing so. I found some midwives who were furtively campaigning for changes, desperate for a midwifery model, desperate for women to have choice both within and outside the system. At one stage I went into hospital with a woman and met a midwife wanting to move into homebirth. Over the years, despite us having our differences, she has been a strong ally and has 'walked the walk' of wanting to change things. Initially this was extremely important. There were many people 'talking the talk' but when you asked them to actually put their hands up and start to change things there would be a deathly silence. This other midwife truly practised what she preached. I then had a number of women starting to ring me wanting care when they had complex issues. I started to feel torn. How do we stay within our scope of practice, our comfort zone, but still support women wanting our care? Al was one of these women.

Al had had four previous caesareans and struggled to find care that supported her choices inside or outside the system. Eventually Al found a midwife to care for her and went on to have an (undiagnosed) vaginal breech at home. There were many issues around this. The hospital became aware of her case and involved child services. Al's midwife was not a registered midwife and all sorts of suggestions were made regarding disciplinary action for her. I felt shocked; had I somehow caused this to happen by not providing the care that was needed for Al?

After this, I had a radical change of thought process. I needed to dig my heels in and felt that it was time to face the hospitals and doctors head on. So I did. I started to support women who were going head to head with the hospital. I continued to think about what the evidence says is safe care, but I didn't worry about the rhetoric that was being dished up about safety, particularly around homebirth for low risk women. I also started to look at what the woman's rights are, and what is needed to ensure that care is safe for her. I started talking extensively to consumer groups about what was needed for change to occur and we all started to talk to the media and get them on our side. Other midwives in our area were gaining momentum too spurred on by some of the victories at a State and Federal level. It felt like the winds of change were finally going to arrive in the region where I live.

Not long after this I was at a stall at a local parenting event when a woman walked up to me. She asked me if I had ever heard of having a vaginal birth after two caesarean sections. We had a brief discussion where I encouraged her to come and see me. Gen had her first baby aged 19 in a private hospital in Brisbane. She thought that by 'going private' she would receive the best care. She now knew, at nearly 30, that the care she received was not great. She never laboured and had only had a few hours of contractions before the interventions started. I listened to her story of this first birth which is like so many other first births in private hospitals; once there is an offer of a caesarean it sounds like the most appealing thing to do. Gen had her second baby five years later in a major teaching hospital in London. She was told that her pelvis was small and she was sent for pelvimetry, which reflected this. She then had another caesarean. Another five years passed and she was pregnant again and thinking that she could have a vaginal birth. She really wanted it. We went to the hospital a number of times trying to negotiate how she could be cared for. At this point the hospital had only allowed one woman to have a 'trial' of a vaginal birth after two caesareans. It had gone badly. I prepared Gen for what she would face, tales of dire gloom, potential death of mother and baby. She was told that she 'must' sign a document saying she would come in in labour, have a cannula in labour and be monitored continuously. Gen signed the form, but we doubted that the hospital could or would reinforce the document.

Gen explored her feelings relating to the birth really well. We discussed constantly how Gen felt about having another caesarean and what she really wanted. The pressure was intense but Gen was certainly one cool woman. She was able to detach from the 'stress' of the hospital putting pressure on her, particularly towards the end of the pregnancy. This stress increased Gen's determination. At 41 weeks of pregnancy, we were starting to sweat, the hospital were telling us that Gen would 'have' to have a caesarean section if she wasn't in labour by the Monday. Finally, after lots of walking, intercourse, hot curry and every other trick in the book things started to shift.

We often wondered whether it was just the determination that she did not want to end up with another caesarean but Gen rang me in the early hours of the Sunday morning before she was due to go back to the hospital. I attended immediately just for reassurance. We stayed at home for a long time with Gen in active labour, doing her own thing. She was doing really well, mostly quietly labouring in the lounge. Gen was really 'in the zone' for this labour and needed little support or encouragement. She was quiet and moved as she needed to, adopting positions which conserved energy, she prepared herself in case there were many hours ahead. The night was spent mostly in dark silence – her husband slept, as she wanted, and her sister and I quietly stayed close by.

In the wee hours of the morning Gen felt ready to go to hospital. We got there and were met by an understanding registrar who didn't push the issue of a cannula. Inserting a cannula was something that Gen felt wasn't actually being used to keep her 'safe' but was really an admission that they did not think she would have a vaginal birth. Gen agreed to have monitoring, which actually was terrible. But her husband and I helped her to move around a lot. The determination that Gen had to stay in the same space that she was in at home was amazing. She never ever faltered, and when she was spoken to she just nodded or shook her head at any staff coming into the room. She was completely focused. Initially we had a student midwife allocated to us. It was great for the student and it was great for us.

Gen moved towards birth very quickly and started to push her baby out. Once Gen was pushing she used a bar that she hung off, which helped her to open her pelvis well. It was a wonderful moment to see this beautiful baby boy born vaginally with his amazed Dad looking on. He was much heavier than both his brothers and Gen felt amazing. We were all crying, as we knew what a triumph this was for Gen and for other women in this situation.

A few moments after the birth, while Gen was still sitting on a birth stool, resting and nursing her baby, which was still attached to her, one of the most difficult obstetricians came in to the room and said, 'Oh, have you just had a baby? You have had two previous caesarean sections haven't you? Well I am glad you are safe.' And with that he left.

It might only sound like a small victory, but I believe that this was where things truly started to turn. We were all elated; everyone knew about this woman, she was a hero. She still is. One of the hospital-based midwives, who was there for the birth, has since commenced working in a one-to-one model. I am sure that this birth had an impact on her, as it did on me. I could really see how the stars were lining up or how the house of cards was beginning to topple, depending on which way you want to look at it. A midwifery model looked closer.

Al rang me; she was pregnant once more. We discussed her options. What could she do in the local region? We went to the hospital. There was no way that they would support her. She tried other hospitals close by. They were not supportive either. We knew they could not 'refuse' her but she didn't want to walk into a battleground at the moment of birth. And that is what it would have been. The thought of a homebirth frightened Al because of the transfer and because of child services. She did not want child services to take the other children. What could we do?

I thought of a supportive obstetric colleague from my distant past whom I had seen at various conferences and was well known for his support of complex situations. I phoned him and explained that Al was now in her seventh pregnancy, that she had had four caesareans but that baby number two and baby number six had been vaginal births, with baby number six being a breech at home. He said that she would have to come and meet him but that he would be happy to care for her, to stay on call for her (no mean feat as he was working in a major teaching hospital as Director by this stage) and to get her to phone him. This obstetrician worked in another State. After several calls Al travelled over 1000km by plane with all six children, her mother and her partner to meet this obstetrician. She travelled to see him again at 36 weeks, rented a house and stayed there until she had her baby vaginally two weeks later. The obstetrician subsequently organised a conference of both obstetricians and midwives and spoke of this case. He said how ridiculous it was that a woman had to travel so far, across States, due to fear and an inability to find care that met her needs. It reminded me that we still had a long way to go.

As the tide changed, the situation started to look much rosier. The hospital established, on a shoe string, without resources, a midwifery model of care. Homebirth practice in the district flourished. Women were coming out of the woodwork saying what they wanted. The consumer movement pressed on, demanding more and more change. My involvement on a political level increased and my focus became advocacy, taking me to some degree away from the clinical side of things. The women coming now didn't realise that they were getting so many choices.

Then I found out I was having another baby. Many of the old doubts started to rise within. Having had significant polyhydramnios with my two other babies, I was worried. Should I have this one at home? Could I have midwifery care? Would any of the obstetricians support midwives to care for me? Did I need an obstetrician at all? I had polyhydramnios with every pregnancy; it was just my way of doing it. Why should anyone else need to be involved? But this time it was different. There were no pushy people telling me what to do. The obstetric support of my midwife was completely different and my amazing midwives were able to show their faces, without being run out of town. We had a wonderful homebirth of our beautiful girl in water, no problems from the excess amniotic fluid. We are still basking in this four months later as I write.

We aren't at the end of the road. There is still a long way to go and probably lots of bends, some of which can't even be seen yet but when I am reminded to look through the rear-view mirror at the road behind I can see we have changed forever the landscape of birth in our area.

Holly's story (Midwife)

Tales – so many tales – how to decide on one? The most vivid stories for me always come from my earliest days as I learned how to be a midwife. I was so green and so untrusting after years of working in critical care. I had to consciously learn how to trust birth, trust women, and trust myself. I also had to learn how to manage the obstetric and nursing staff so they would trust me – what a long road it was, filled with laughter, tears of frustration, but mostly joy in the work.

My first position was in a thriving midwifery group that worked for a health maintenance organisation with wonderfully supportive midwives. We shared hospital call among the four of us. The weekends were the longest, starting at 6pm on Friday and ending at 8am on Monday. I used to race from my Friday clinic to get to the hospital in time for dinner to ensure my energy for the days and nights ahead. I quickly learned how to pace myself, finding that four hours was a magic number for sleep, and when you didn't get that, a shower was almost as good. Usually the births would space themselves out, but sometimes they didn't – like the weekend I had four nullips back to back.

The night stories, for some reason are the ones that come to surface most quickly. I wonder why – perhaps it is because there are fewer intrusions – it's just you and the woman with no postpartum rounds or clinics to worry about. I can still hear the ominous sound of one obstetrician's clogs coming down the hall – a sign to me to shuttle the woman into the bathroom so he couldn't intrude. All the labour rooms in the hospital where I worked had TVs in them and people sure watch a lot of weird stuff to entertain themselves in the middle of the night. One time I told a father I simply could not help bring a baby into the world in the midst of a gory vampire movie – fortunately the mother agreed with me.

I loved the long talks with families as they laboured. You got to know people so well as they talked about their plans, their worries, their families, jobs, pets (and their adjustment to the new baby). The list of subjects was endless. I always sat in the room with the woman as I reviewed her prenatal record. There's always that question, 'Do you know if you're having a boy or girl?' One beaming couple answered yes and told me the name of the coming child. I smiled and nodded, continuing to read the record. As I got to the last section I reviewed the amniocentesis report – the inevitable 46xx or 46xy. My eyes widened and I queried them again about the baby's gender. It was not the same – someone had given them the wrong information and they had been planning for a baby of the opposite sex for 20 weeks. At this point I excused myself and went out into the hall to compose my inwardly frantic thoughts. I returned to the room and gently said I had some news to share with them. They handled it very well and were able to move beyond the news to concentrate on a joyful birth. I forever after read amniocentesis reports three times before telling people the results.

One night I remember calling my mentor at home to strategise my ability to attend two women's births who were labouring neck and neck (one multip at 8cm and one nullip fully dilated). I was the only midwife on duty and if they birthed at the same time one would have an obstetrician attend her – something neither woman wanted. Her advice, 'Break that multip's bag and get on with it!', was sound advice and they had their babies about 15 minutes apart.

Then there was the time when I almost lost my life in the midwife's call room. We had a tiny room next to the in-hospital birth centre with a set of bunk beds. It had been a long weekend and I had attended several arduous labours. I was catching a couple winks of sleep in the bottom bunk while waiting for a nullip to get to the hospital. A midwife colleague from another practice crept into the room and clambered up to the top bunk. Just as she did my beeper went off and I sat up. Bang – the top bunk crashed, midwife and all, down on the bottom bunk. We all escaped unscathed. But of all the memories and stories, one has stood out for many, many years because it was a turning point and an immense learning experience for me.

We were still learning how to care for the number of Southeast Asian families who had immigrated to our city. I was on night duty and had not met this woman before she came in in labour. She was a grand multip in her early forties. Several older women and her daughter, a woman of childbearing age, were supporting her. When I examined her my heart sank – she had a transverse lie. She was in very active labour, but her membranes were intact. Her daughter helped translate and I told them I needed to have the obstetrician examine her. They nodded and I left the room in search of my colleague.

This was one of my favourite obstetricians, always willing to listen to my plans of care, even when they didn't precisely reflect unit protocols – as long as I had a solid rationale. However, this was out of my league and I knew we didn't have a lot of options. She reminded me that trying an external version was not considered a safe option if a woman was in active labour. We went back into the room and the obstetrician confirmed my assessment. She proceeded to explain the situation to the four women in the room while the nurse and I listened. She said the woman would need a caesarean delivery. The woman and her two older attendants shook their heads – this was not what they wanted. The daughter, uncertainly, asked them if it might not be a good idea. The discussion went on for about 20 minutes. Finally, the women said they could not make the final decision until their village elder was consulted. They made arrangements to call him.

As we waited to embrace this cultural need of the family we did our best not to pace, either inside or outside of the room as this woman continued to labour. Of course our worry was that she would rupture her membranes and prolapse a cord or arm and we would be faced with a need for immediate action.

As the time stretched on we began to realise that the older women's support of this woman was changing. They had been massaging her arms and shoulders, but now they had moved to her abdomen. I was struck by the similarity of their facial wrinkles with the looseness of this woman's abdomen with a baby not filling out the contours because of its lie. Then suddenly I sensed that their hands had a different purpose than comfort – they had literally taken things into their own hands and were turning the baby. I caught the eye of the obstetrician and she was on to it as well. At a loss, we said nothing and sat down.

Slowly, the contour of the woman's abdomen changed – we checked with our hands and then with ultrasound; the baby was vertex. There was a knock on the door – it was the village elder. Laughing and weeping, every woman in that room thanked him for coming but we no longer needed him. It was a lovely birth.

As the obstetrician and I talked about it afterwards we both admitted our discomfort, but felt it was OK to step aside. Although counter to our training we both had one of those moments that tells you training isn't everything. I learned to trust women and realised that my best action was to provide the safe space for this to happen – I didn't have to 'do' anything. The obstetrician and I remained present, but with conscious 'inaction'. I was forever grateful that it was this obstetrician who was on duty with me that night and that she was willing to trust her instincts and the women's wisdom in the room.

Andrew's story (Obstetrician)

My story is about waterbirthing. I am an obstetrician in Australia and have been in private practice for many years looking after women having babies in private hospitals. Our typical model of care involves antenatal care in a doctor's office and care in labour in hospital by that doctor. However women have a hospital-employed midwife with them throughout labour and the doctor generally attends at the end of labour at the time of the birth.

The hospital where I have practised in recent times is modern and somewhat upmarket and has a very well-equipped maternity section. There are three delivery suites and 12 postnatal rooms with double beds and women generally stay in about five days postnatally. When it was built small spas were included in each birthing suite for water immersion, but waterbirth was not happening at all. Gradually, a desire for women to use the spas for waterbirthing was recognised and I and the hospital midwives became interested in providing this option. At the time there were two other obstetricians on the staff, each running his own private practice but we covered each other at weekends on a one-in-three roster. As it panned out, my two colleagues did not develop an interest in waterbirthing while I became an enthusiast.

I saw the benefits of waterbirthing and was comfortable letting the natural process of birthing proceed while still watching for any signs of problems and only intervening when necessary. I found the women whom I was supervising were very much appreciative of this way of having a baby and they seemed to have a very positive feeling about their birth upon reflection afterwards. I felt that I had to trust in the process of natural birth and let it proceed rather than control it in any way. This lack of being the controlling person and having to sit back and do nothing may be why waterbirth does not appeal to many doctors.

Although waterbirth really took hold at our hospital, and the midwives, with few exceptions, all became experienced and enthusiastic, there was one aspect that became a problem. For the first time there was now a difference in the way I conducted obstetrics as opposed to my two colleagues. This meant that two out of every three weekends my patients who wanted waterbirth could not do so unless I was prepared to come in on my weekends off. So, essentially I was under pressure to be on call all the time, day and night, seven days a week. I did that for two years and found it quite challenging. However the other reality was that I was under the pressure of working in a way that my colleagues did not agree with. Another awkward situation was that there were women attending the other two obstetricians who wanted to change doctors so that they may have the chance of a waterbirth, and I soon became overbooked due to women coming to my practice having heard about the waterbirth option.

The situation eventually resolved as the two colleagues ceased practising obstetrics and two new obstetricians arrived who did offer waterbirth. So we were back to a situation where all three doctors could share on call duties in the normal way. Also, the hospital could now say that waterbirth was offered to all clients and it could now be openly discussed in the hospital-based antenatal classes, which was not previously possible. Some time later we were up to 25% of all births occurring under water.

Jayne came to see me for antenatal and obstetric care in her first pregnancy. She was one of the midwives in the birthing unit where I worked. Her story illustrates how I tried to manage things in my obstetric practice. Here is her story in her own words.

Jayne's story

When I fell pregnant with Louis in 2002, my time practising as a midwife had led me to assume that I would have a spontaneous vaginal delivery. I didn't give caesarean section much thought, even when I found out I was having a big baby.

I had been with many women in labour and delivery and really wanted to experience it for myself and, in my eyes, 'do it properly'. I was induced at term, which in hindsight I wouldn't do again. I know now that I probably wasn't ready but patience was running out.

Labour was slow and progress slow too, but no syntocinon was needed. I only used entonox and was doing all right but got into difficulty [Jayne was 6cm dilated with meconium liquor] and needed a caesarean. I don't think I felt disappointed, just relieved and excited. So it wasn't a real issue at the time. The post-op wound infection wasn't great but otherwise all went well and breastfeeding (my other wish) was great and I breastfed for two years.

I think it helped that I did labour for 14 hours, so at least I experienced that side of things.

When I fell pregnant with Duke, I was immediately determined to try for a vaginal birth after caesarean in the water. I remember telling midwife colleagues and them saying, 'Of course you will have a Caesarean', and this made me more determined to have the waterbirth I wanted. At my first visit with Dr Davidson I brought the subject up and was so relieved that it was possible. It was made clear that it carried risks, especially in view of the wound infection, but the discussion was positive. I remember later in the pregnancy signing a form stating that I understood the risks, and my husband and I were relieved. My husband knew how much it meant to me and was 100% supportive.

At 36 weeks I had a pelvimetry to check the pelvic size and it checked out ok, confirming a vaginal delivery was a viable option. When I went into spontaneous labour, I was taken straight in to the waterbirth suite and it was comforting to know that everyone seemed to know how I wanted it to work and was on board with it (although they still thought I would end up getting out for the birth).

I had an artificial rupture of membranes and didn't get into the pool for a while, and when I did it slowed things down so I got out again, which was much better. There was a nursing shift change and eventually I started feeling some low pressure so re-entered the pool. The water was warm and comforting and I felt weightless. I recall the new midwife telling me that I had progressed to full dilatation and I remained in the water, mainly on my hands and knees, draped over the edge of the pool with the entonox pipe firmly in my grasp. At no point did it cross my mind to get out and I can honestly say I gave no thought to my caesarean scar, I just trusted that if something felt wrong I would get out. I think I pushed for a couple of hours and his head eventually began to crown. In between contractions, I recall thinking, 'I'm doing it, I'm actually doing it!' When his head was delivered I really appreciated the hands off approach. I just did not want to be touched, so when the cord was confirmed not to be around his neck, we just waited. It was so peaceful, and I could see his head in the mirror that was below me which was great and this urged me to push him out. He lay on my chest for a while with the cord intact while we checked each other out; it was just wonderful.

I felt that I had completed labour and birth the way it should be; calm, quiet, and as hands-off as possible. I felt no fear through labour and felt supported in my wishes. No-one even mentioned getting out of the pool, and the midwives' confidence gave me comfort and confidence in return.

Looking back, I am so proud to say that I had a caesarean and then a waterbirth. It wasn't really that I was 'allowed' to do so, but that there was trust in the natural process and I was given a chance for this to happen. I will always be deeply grateful for that opportunity and I still feel empowered and ready to deal with anything.

Jayne's story shows how women commonly feel very positive about the experience after waterbirth. This was very rewarding from my perspective. Offering waterbirth as an option certainly enhanced my obstetric practice, and fitted with my desire to avoid intervention as much as possible and to keep the caesarean rate as low as possible. I would say though that practising this way was more demanding, as there was less reliance on reaching for the forceps or the knife as a way to end a labour or get home to bed.

When we began offering the waterbirth option we had small corner spas, which only had room for the mother and did not have much room for her to move about. Birthing women were restricted to mostly staying in a few positions, mostly floating on their back, kneeling, or sometimes squatting. Space was very limited around the spa as well, but nevertheless we successfully conducted our first 300 waterbirths in these quite cramped conditions. The essential point I feel was that the woman was submerged in warm water and derived the benefits. Family members were able to be very involved and close, while the woman had the advantage of her own personal space in the water.

We subsequently designed and built a large pool for water immersion and waterbirth in one of the three delivery areas. This was where Jayne gave birth to Duke. It was round and about two metres across and 580mm deep with steps and a bench on one side. We had quite a few problems with the local health authorities who needed to approve the installation, and also had a number of plumbing issues as the hospital had not done this type of thing before. However once the new larger pool was ready it became evident that it was far superior to the old smaller shallower spas. From that time onwards, the midwives would use the new pool rather than the spas, even if it meant swapping women from one delivery suite to another during labour.

Women labouring in the new pool now had freedom to move about and adopted all sorts of different positions, and in about half the cases, their partners would also be in the pool. For the actual birth, women commonly were reclining, supported by their partners, kneeling while leaning outwards over the edge of the pool, squatting while holding handles attached to the pool sides, or sitting with their backs against the edge of the pool. We sometimes had to ask the women to move towards the side of the pool as the baby emerged, so that we could reach the infant after the birth, as attendants could not reach the middle of the pool without overbalancing. (We did have one occasion when a doctor fell in.)

Women seemed much more comfortable in the larger pool, and women who had babies in both a spa and the new pool definitely preferred the latter. Our approach was very much 'hands off' for the actual birth. We also avoided 'coaching' and generally just let the mother birth the baby herself without too much verbal direction. With that policy it was interesting to compare the outcomes in relation to vagino-perineal trauma in women having waterbirths and those delivering spontaneously out of water. We kept data on this and found both groups were similar in this respect. Approximately 50% needed some suturing whether waterbirth or 'dry' birth. This contrasts with other waterbirth centres I have visited.

Our data collection showed outcomes generally were very good in the waterbirth group as far as mother and baby were concerned. This, of course, is what you would expect, as women who deliver in the water are having spontaneous births without complications – otherwise they would not be in the water for the birth. Also one should be aware that if there were an adverse neonatal outcome, it probably would not have been caused by the water per se, and may have been the same if the birth had occurred out of water.

Looking back on nearly 10 years of waterbirths at our hospital, I remember the various obstacles to establishing such a service, but the problems encountered along the way are outweighed by the excellent outcomes and the enormous satisfaction gained by the women, such as Jayne, who birth in this way.

Joan's story (Midwife)

For women, the birth of their baby is a life-changing event. For the midwife who is with the women, each birth provides experiences and opportunities for learning about practice and for deepening the understanding of it. Sometimes for the midwife too, the birth can be life changing.

The story that I am going to tell you is one such story. It was life changing for me, not because of the birth itself, which was a physiological, uninterrupted birth at home, but because of the questions it demanded that I face and answer. This birth came at a time in my practice when I was beginning to question how I, as a midwife, was experiencing the context of birth. Despite New Zealand's acceptance of midwifery-led care and of homebirth, I had a sense that there was an increasing amount of fear and anxiety around birth and that this might be leading to our increasing levels of intervention. I felt increased fear and anxiety myself and this was beginning in some sense to spoil birth for me. I wondered if others felt the same. But let me begin the story and you will start to see the questions and issues that arose.

This is the story of Bronwen and David and the birth of Hanna, their fourth baby. Bron and Pete popped in to visit me early in their pregnancy to see if I might be able to be their midwife. Although Bronwen's first baby was born by caesarean section, she had since had two subsequent homebirths with no difficulty. She wanted to have this baby at home too, so I saw no real difficulties in supporting their decision for a homebirth. We agreed on a time to make a full booking and to begin pregnancy care. Just as they were leaving David said to Bronwen, 'Oh, did you tell Joan about the diabetes?'

Thus began for us all an interesting time. For me it was to prove both challenging and rewarding. I was then, and still am, completely supportive of the homebirth option for healthy women and babies. Fifteen years of working with deliveries at home have taught me a great deal about birth and I firmly believe that healthy birth belongs at home. This birth for me, however seemed to move beyond the realms of the 'low risk'. Gestational diabetes in association with a previous caesarean section would be considered by many as 'risk factors' which should preclude a homebirth. This birth was certainly going to stretch and challenge me. Bronwen had had midwifery support for her previous pregnancy when the gestational diabetes had been discovered. What was I going to do, how might I go about making this decision and how would I justify it?

What I felt I had to consider was, 'What if something goes wrong?' I first had to somehow quantify the risk. For Bronwen and her baby there were the risks of uterine rupture, shoulder dystocia, hypoglycaemia and sudden fetal death. There were also risks if she had her baby in hospital: induction, caesarean section, separation from the baby, formula feeds for the baby, iatrogenic infection, emotional dislocation and distress. How were we to calculate and balance these risks and whose decision was it? I had to consider Bronwen and David's decision and ask how my input might be considered as relevant to this decision; I had to ask myself whether we would trust each other with the decision; and I had to consider my own risk if I was to support this birth at home. After a lot of research I decided that in Bronwen's situation it was not possible to calculate the risk. All we could surmise was that if the gestational diabetes was well controlled with diet alone, the risk of adverse outcome for Bronwen or her baby was very small. By this stage, Bronwen was clearly getting the message that I was fearful and she suggested that we all get together to talk about it. It was here, in the context of frank discussion that we discovered, uncovered, discussed, unpacked, and, at last, accepted risk. My anxieties and fears dissipated somewhat and I was able to be with Bronwen in a more relaxed manner. What I came to understand was that, in fact, the sociocultural context was more risky than the birth itself and that it was this that was making me anxious. In a sense Bronwen had a head start on me in that she had had to deal with the risk issues in her previous pregnancy. She and David had already worked through these in some depth. It took me a while to catch up. Hearing that Bronwen and David understood my risk and were prepared to accommodate it in their decisions helped. They were also committed to not putting their baby at unnecessary risk should we begin to identify possible difficulties. We began to trust each other more and I relaxed into the birth.

So what happened in the end? Bronwen consulted with the diabetic clinic and her gestational diabetes remained well controlled with a modified diet. At my request she consulted with the obstetrician (my risk covered). He said that as long as her diabetes remained well controlled and that she delivered at 38 weeks, she would not need intervention from him, but that if she went beyond 38 weeks she would need to reconsider her plans for her birth and see him again. At 38 weeks to the day Hanna very obligingly decided to be born. After a couple of days of on and off pre-labour, Bronwen's labour established and Hanna was born at home, surrounded by her family and friends. All was well. Hanna breast fed almost continually for the first few hours and Bronwen had a wonderful supply of colostrum. Who knows what would have happened had the pregnancy gone to full term? Thank goodness we didn't have to find out.

So what did I learn and what changed for me? This birth took me to the edge of my practice, a place where we can sometimes get clear vision, a place where we can often best examine and critique our practice and our perspectives. Homebirth often does this. This birth touched issues of choice, of agency, of relationship, and of responsibility. I came face to face with my fear and had to name it. For me this birth lifted the concept of risk to the fore. Risk, then, became for me a notion that needed to be unpacked and dealt with. I began to see how contextual risk is often determined not so much by the science as by the context in which life is experienced and understood. I saw that risk and how it is defined and managed are political issues, fundamentally related to power and control. It highlighted for me the uncertainty of birth and of life with which we must deal. What is also clear in this story is the complexity of midwifery. Nothing is ever simple. We provide care for women who have many different perspectives and needs. All must be taken into account. Sometimes we do not know the answers. We also need to collaborate with other health professionals, all of whom have their own perspectives. And of course we work in a complex social and cultural environment. All this is anything but simple. We have multiple arenas of accountability: the woman and her family, our peers, the maternity provider institutions, and the community. There are also issues of power and control. The midwife needs to consider whose knowledge is seen as authoritative and who has the power to make decisions. The midwife weaves her care in ways that best meet the needs of the woman while at the same time acknowledging the demands of the environment in which she works. I saw that the context in which risk occurs has a huge impact on how risk is experienced and that the context of risk for the mother and her family can be at odds with the context or perspective of risk for the midwife. I learned that I really needed a conscious awareness of my own position on risk in order to negotiate risk with the mother and mediate with the perspectives of obstetrics.

It also highlighted that I really needed to know what I was doing. I needed to summon all my skills. I needed to be able to access and assess the research, and to be able to communicate this. My skills of assessment needed to be astute and I needed to be accountable for the decisions I made in light of this. I had to work with the context in which this birth unfolded, understanding the political nature of birth. I needed to 'work the system' to get the best and safest experience for Bronwen and her baby, while at the same time maintaining my own safety within the medico legal context. In some sense this was real evidence-based practice in action. What I discovered was that whether we like it or not risk does play an important place in the lives and practice of midwives. We may try to escape or avoid the techno-rational, medical birth of hospital but the processes of accountability with which we must deal remain fundamentally focused through a techno-rational lens – that of obstetrics. We need to be canny about how we deal with this. What women choose to avoid, we often cannot.

Above all this story brought to light for me the centrality of the 'with womenness' of midwifery. If we keep this central, no matter how the women may be positioned, we can use our skills and work the system in order to support her to have the best possible birth. This is of course what we are all about, often undertaking this in a complex and unpredictable context. I sometimes wonder if the women for whom we care appreciate the complexity of the care that we provide and the enormous diversity of perspectives and world views that we mediate, or even whether it is important that they do. I think that Bronwen and David did understand some of this and it was this that helped me to support them in their decision. There are many gifts in midwifery. Sometimes they are unexpected. It is sometimes the hard ones that reap the best rewards. Bronwen and David's decision to birth at home and to ask me along, and to trust me to help was one such gift. The central question for me was how do we as midwives make sense of our work given the risk context in which we live? In response to the stories that the midwives told me I developed a framework that might help support us in our work. This framework is a three-legged birth stool, not for the women, but this time for the midwife. The seat is the 'being with' the woman and the three legs of the stool, the parts that give support, I have called 'working as a professional', (which is all about being skilled and accountable), 'working the system' and 'working with complexity'. The struts that hold the stool together I call storytelling.

For me birth at home is the place where I can get some clear thinking, where birth is revealed for what it is and where midwifery can be most artfully and skilfully practised. What this experience did for me was to make me face fear head on and to work with it rather than avoid it. Somehow, accepting fear and putting it into context was in some sense liberating. I was able to do this only within the relationship that I had with Bronwen and David. Just as I accept the possibility and the love inherent in birth, so too must I accept and make sense of risk and fear.

CHAPTER 9

Tales from fathers and siblings

Bruce's story (Father)

A piece of the furniture

Morning, Wednesday 27th October 2004: Mount Glorious, South-East Queensland, Australia, a little house in the forest. My wife Erika is pregnant, and past her due date by six or seven days, 13 days if you take the earlier date. Due dates are so dodgy.

I'm not anxious about the baby or Erika, but I am anxious. I am booked to attend a big meeting in Rockhampton on Saturday for the review of maternity services in Queensland. I've bought the plane ticket and I'm not sure what to do – if the baby doesn't come today or tomorrow I'll have to cancel. This review is a big thing for us, we've put in years of lobbying and activism to get things here, and I feel stressed about it. I'm also anxious because I feel exposed about this birth. I meet regularly with many people who think that birth is a dangerous event needing medical control in a big hospital, and who would consider a homebirth to be a foolish gamble. We're trying to set the policy direction for maternity care in Queensland, and if anything went wrong in Erika's birth, it would be well known, would look really bad, and would affect the process. I'm anxious for the reform process which means so much to so many of us.

I'm not actually anxious about the birth for the baby, or for Erika. Erika is an expert birther – this is her third baby and she has prepared thoroughly. Our first baby, Jasper, is now eight and was born here at home, while we were building the house (isn't that always the way?). Erika had an 'anterior lip' of her cervix in the way for a while when labouring, but with her midwife's expert guidance she held back her pushing until the way was clear, and Jasper was born into my hands.

Our second, Rose, was more unusual. Rose was breech – backside instead of head first. Rose's pregnancy was a stressful time in our relationship, mostly because of me dealing with Erika dealing with pregnancy, I think. A midwife told me that breeches were often due to 'something upside-down in your life', which seemed to fit. We tried massage and a few tricks to turn

Rose around during late pregnancy, but she didn't want to turn and Erika didn't want to hassle her. Planning a breech birth at home caused some stress – in anticipation – with some of my family, but Erika knew that if she went to hospital with a breech pregnancy she would either have a caesarean, or a big ugly fight about it with the doctors. Rose was born at home, very peacefully – easier than Jasper coming head-first! I didn't catch Rose, because Erika and the midwife had worked out the optimal position of Erika leaning on me at that time.

I've been studying the scientific evidence regarding birth pretty intensely over recent years. Bad outcomes can happen in births, whatever you do. Babies die, are disabled; women die or are injured. These bad outcomes are rare now that we have good health and good health care when we need it. The evidence about the relative safety of homebirth is very clear. In a normal birth, with access to a hospital when needed, the risks to baby or mother are no higher at home than in hospital. That is unless you consider the risks of caesarean or other stressful interventions, which are much higher in hospital.

If something did go wrong, we could deal with it as a family, as everyone must. So I knew my anxiety was just anxiety – there was nothing to be done about it – except try to wind it down. Erika has been a little unsettled, but not anxious. She loves being pregnant, and this is a very much wanted baby, following a long wait for conception. Erika is beautiful and big and ripe.

At 10.00pm on the 27th October Erika, Jasper, Rose and I are all in our big family bed – side-by-side mattresses on low bases. Erika has just left the bed, telling me that her waters have broken (she knew she was in labour when we went to bed, but kept it secret). I asked her if she wanted me to do anything, but she doesn't. I probably won't be able to sleep, but I should rest as much as possible. Erika has everything prepared. There are towels and sheets and plans for who should be called when. The rainbow-coloured inflatable kids' pool is ready for me to blow up – we tested it a few weeks ago. The fitting I use to connect a hose to the kitchen tap is ready.

When I do get up, my first job is to light the woodstove. I need to make the house warm, and the stove also heats our hot water – filling the birth pool uses a lot. I also put a few big pots and kettles full of water on the stove top. Next job is inflating the pool. This time we have a little pump so I don't go dizzy blowing it up by mouth like last time. Our heavy tarp is on the floor to catch splashes (although it won't help if the pool bursts – which did happen to a friend). In between jobs I take some photos. I have the camera on my Grandfather's tripod, so there's no flash and Erika doesn't notice me. Erika asks me to hide the clock, to remove the mental stimulation. I keep checking the pool water temperature as the water rises, and stoking the fire. As pots warm, I tip them into the pool, and refill them. As I do my jobs, Erika labours quietly.

The house is sparsely lit, and mostly dark. Erika moves from the darkened sitting area, where she has been kneeling and leaning on the couch, and goes outside to stand on the deck in the light of the full moon. We hardly talk or touch. Erika knows what to do, and I know my job is to make sure she can get on with it without distraction. I am like a piece of the furniture. No-one but Erika and me know this is happening. The kids are sleeping, the neighbours can't see our lights. Our family life is changing forever, but it's our own story for now. When Erika is ready, she asks me to phone Amanda and Jodi. Amanda will drive 10km along the ridge from Mt Nebo, and look after our children so Erika and I can remain focused. Jodi is Erika's midwife, and must drive 30km up the mountain from Samsonvale, in the valley below. The night is so quiet that we can hear Amanda's car as she reaches the ridge. Some of our neighbours hear her too and guess what is happening. Hearing Amanda's car, Erika retreats to the dark little space between the piano and the couch, where the kids often play with their blocks. I greet Amanda at the door and send her downstairs to rest until she is needed. Erika is starting to moan. It's not pain. Transition is coming. Erika steps into the pool, which has remained the focus of much of my attention, and which is just 37 degrees. She is on hands and knees, rocking, frowning, moaning, completely focused inward. Erika asks me to call Georgina, her friend (also a midwife), who lives just up the hill. Jodi arrives, cracking a quiet joke on her way in. Erika stands briefly while Jodi checks the baby's heart rate. Georgina arrives with her baby in a sling.

Erika is crouching in the water and asks Jodi if she can push yet. She doesn't want to push too soon and run into a cervical lip as she did with Jasper. Jodi gives her the nod. I know the baby will be here soon, so I call to Amanda to bring out the children. Amanda has been awake all along, and the children have been too for some time, listening to Erika's moans. Rose woke immediately already having dreamed about Erika being in labour, Jasper was roused and they come out, very excited, but silent, and sit together with Amanda, close to the pool.

It is 2.15am, Erika didn't plan to birth in the water, but decides to at the last minute (but neither did she plan not to). With Erika there are no expectations – she does what comes – the baby will be born in the water. She is on hands and knees in the pool. I will have to catch the baby in the water, so I move behind Erika and watch the baby crowning under water. The baby pops out, and I catch it and lift it out of the water, and hand it to Erika. My lack of experience with waterbirths is evident here – the baby's cord is now wrapped around Erika's leg – but Erika manages anyway. Erika cuddles her new baby and croons to it.

There are no strong expressions of emotion as with the other births – it's all so peaceful and natural. Our new baby – a boy – cries. Our other babies didn't cry at birth, so we are a little surprised. Erika gives him his first feed, still in the bath. He then puts his thumb into his mouth – also a first for our babies. He must have been doing this inside. Afterwards we found that Jodi had picked up the camera, and had taken some precious photos of the birth and the first cuddle. We didn't even notice the flashes.

Erika leaves the bath and lies down to feed the baby some more and wait for the placenta. She untangles the cord too. It is semi-dark over here. Jodi and I help Jasper to cut the cord after it stops pulsing. The placenta comes soon. Jodi's presence is unobtrusive. She has been doing assessments and taking notes, but we haven't noticed. Georgina leaves. I phone Erika's Mum to tell her the news. She's been awake all night waiting (how did she know?) and will be staying with us for a week or so to help. I recommend she get some sleep before starting the long drive. Erika has a shower, with Jodi's help. Amanda and Jodi clean up while Erika and the baby tuck into bed together. After Amanda leaves Jodi checks and weighs our baby and soon after goes home. Jodi will be back daily for the next few days, and take good care of Erika and baby. By 4.00am everyone has gone. We are all going back to the family bed for a little sleep. Now we are five.

A famous obstetrician, Michel Odent, who is regarded as one of the fathers of the natural birth movement, recently wrote about why fathers should never be at the birth of their child. Odent's approach was provocative enough to stimulate much discussion about the effect fathers have on birthing women – a conversation I feel is necessary. It is hard to judge Odent's proposition from my experience. My circumstances have not been the norm for fathers at births. Most find themselves in a big, completely unfamiliar hospital, surrounded by strangers, confused about what's happening and often frightened. I have had the guidance early in fatherhood from our midwife – a strong woman who is clear about what women need in birth. I also have the benefit of Erika's clarity about what she needs. I have witnessed Erika's births in our own home, where I have work to do. Filling the tub, stoking the fire, housekeeping and organising communications have kept my male problem solving mind occupied and diverted from trying to find anything I can help with in the labour and birth. My responsibility as a father to 'defend the space' of his labouring partner has been easy to fulfil. Erika has known that I am there keeping her birthing space private, and keeping distractions at bay. I've been spared the experience men sometimes describe of being in hospital, their wife under siege from staff who want to intervene, and so often left with a sense of failure as husband and protector.

John's story (Father)

On Monday 28th July 2003 at 5.46am at the local hospital Sandra gave birth to our first baby, a beautiful son.

As a healthcare professional working in the emergency setting, it was an experience, about which, for the previous 40 weeks, I had felt anxious and out of control, although I had to put faith and trust in Sandra and her body. Those anxious thoughts and feelings started early on in the pregnancy when Sandra started bleeding at six weeks. The fear of whether this pregnancy was for real or not was quite indescribable. I vividly remember sitting in the Early Pregnancy Unit thinking that I want this to happen so much, but I knew that bleeding was a significantly bad sign. A scan then showed that we were in the very early stages of pregnancy and all seemed well.

During the next 34 weeks we had come to the point where Sandra was going to go into labour and the anxieties in my mind grew stronger. We were prepared very well; we had talked about everything and shared both our thoughts and feelings. Sandra stated to me that if possible she wanted to avoid using pain relief and to remain active during the labour and didn't want to be on a bed. I agreed and if asked in the hospital, I would support her 100% in this decision. The day before the birth Sandra was feeling pains and contractions but nothing strong enough to warrant attending the hospital. Sandra hid these very well because we carried on as normal doing things we would normally do. On the Sunday evening we went to see my parents for a meal and the pain increased but Sandra carried on and we didn't tell the family anything so as not to worry them. On the way home Sandra was convinced it was happening tonight. I can remember feeling I could be a father very soon and then the anxiety of what could happen and the bad thoughts came streaming back.

We arrived home and went to bed but Sandra was very uncomfortable so she decided to have bath. I went downstairs to watch the television. She shouted down to me and I went up to her. During a contraction she had a sudden large gush of blood. At this point I thought, 'What was that?' This was not something I was expecting and my immediate thoughts were to take her to the hospital, Sandra contacted the hospital and after discussion with the midwives it was decided that we would go in.

When we got to the hospital we were met by a midwife who took us to a room and immediately asked Sandra to get on the bed. We declined and asked for the birthing ball, which looked like a large beach ball. We knew that she needed to be checked but the pain was too much at this stage for her to climb onto the bed. However, the midwife listened to the baby's heartbeat, which was fine. When the pain had settled we agreed for her to be examined and the midwife stated she was 8–9cm dilated. I knew this meant we were well on the way. After the examination Sandra got back on the ball and almost immediately she had another strong contraction and her waters broke. At this stage, knowing it was not going to be long, I felt helpless and useless and all I could do was encourage Sandra and tell her I was there and she was doing really well. She did not want me to touch her, rub her back or anything because she was so focused on what she was doing. This is why I believe at this stage women are far stronger than men. She stood up leaning onto the bed for support and I was behind her watching and supporting her, and telling her where we were up to. Another big contraction and I could begin to see the baby's head. It looked a blue colour to me and I became anxious. Another contraction and the face began to show and that was an amazing site. We had created this baby, with God's help. Another push and the baby arrived. I looked over and the baby cried immediately and was passed to Sandra, then we found out it was boy. We knew straight away he was going to be called Jacob. The midwife then wrapped him in a towel and I held my son for the very first time; the emotion was amazing I was so happy, so relieved and just said, 'Hello son, I'm your daddy'. This experience was unbelievable and was so positive. I had only ever heard negative comments about labour, but these are simply a passing memory and only good thoughts now exist.

Our family of three became a family of four on 8th August 2006. This time, however, due to our positive experience of childbirth we decided to plan for a homebirth. When we visited our GP to confirm the pregnancy we were greeted with negative comments and told that as healthcare professionals we should know better. We strongly disagreed and knew that the best place for our next child to be born was in our family home. Following this a midwife visited us at home to do our 'booking'. The midwife was part of a team who would look after us throughout the pregnancy and she was extremely positive about our plan and encouraged us greatly. The anxieties I had previously were remembered but not as strongly, and again I worried about what would happen if something went wrong and we were not at the hospital with the necessary staff and equipment to hand. These were alleviated somewhat through further discussion with Sandra and the midwives who looked after us. Sandra had a good pregnancy and continued working up until 36 weeks. I arranged two weeks annual leave from the due date to be followed, hopefully, by two weeks paternity leave so that we could have as much time as possible together as a family before I had to go back to work. This was not to be.

Sandra went overdue and it was beginning to seem that our homebirth was not going to happen. At that stage I felt disappointed and worried as we so desperately wanted our baby to be born at home. We were given a date for induction and I had to go back to work. It was on my first shift back at work at about 8.30pm that Sandra called me and told me that she was having regular painful contractions and that Jacob had excitedly gone off for a sleepover at Grandma and Grandpa's house. I needed to make my way home. Sandra called the Midwifery-Led Unit to inform them that she was having regular contractions. They asked that we called back when they were coming every five minutes. On the journey home I felt relieved that we were back on course with our plan for a homebirth. I arrived home to find Sandra rocking on the birthing ball and the contractions becoming stronger and more frequent. The next call to the unit was made and a midwife was on her way.

There was a knock on the door and the midwife came in and introduced herself. It wasn't one of our team of midwives but she seemed very pleasant, very confident and very comfortable in her role. I then helped her to carry in all the equipment she might need and ten bags later I was feeling very reassured that she had all possible situations covered. She then sat down with us and asked what we wanted and how we wanted things to go, she also explained that there may be situations when it would be necessary for us to go into the unit. This made us feel in control but also reassured us that plans were in place for all possibilities and that we would be involved in any decision making.

Sandra was 7–8cm dilated when she was examined, and thinking back to Jacob's birth I thought that it wouldn't be long until the baby was born. I was feeling confident and comfortable that things were going well and that once again Sandra was coping well without any pain relief, using her birthing ball and breathing to get her through the contractions. A few hours later it was time for her next examination and Sandra hadn't dilated any further. We discussed this and between the three of us the decision was taken to break her waters as the midwife felt that this would move the labour on. This came with possible consequences and this decision was not taken lightly. It was explained to me that if the waters were found to be stained with meconium it could show that the baby had been stressed at some point in the labour and an ambulance would have to be called and we would be transferred to the unit. Even though we wanted a homebirth desperately, we didn't want our baby's health put at risk and so we decided to proceed. The waters were broken and luckily there was no meconium. Sandra stood up to get back on the birthing ball but immediately felt urges to push and it seemed that the birth was imminent. The midwife called for a second midwife to attend and warned us that she was a bright and bouncy character who would come bounding in. I knew exactly what Sandra was thinking even though she didn't say it. She wouldn't want this at all as she needed to be able to focus on what she was doing without any distractions. However this would not be the case as the urges to push got stronger, and with Sandra standing up and leaning over the back of the armchair the baby's head began to appear. It was at this stage that the midwife said that she needed my help as the pains were making Sandra's legs weak and shaky so we stood at either side of her and supported her. I felt confident and comfortable with this as I'm used to dealing with emergency situations. Another large contraction came and the baby started to come out. I felt a natural instinct to put my hands out and, along with the midwife, I caught the baby as she came out. I held the baby in my arms and noticed it was a girl. She opened her eyes immediately and cried. I felt she was saying, 'Hello, daddy'. The midwife cut the cord and Sandra sat down on the floor and I passed her our daughter. The midwife then wrapped the baby in a towel and I held her while the placenta was delivered. It was an amazing experience to hold our beautiful newborn daughter in our house after catching her as she came into this world. I felt no fear or anxiety during the labour this time as I was involved in the process and wasn't just a spare part.

Shortly after delivering the placenta the second midwife arrived, just as I was having a celebratory drink. She was very surprised by how fast things had happened. The two midwives tidied up their things, ran Sandra a bath while I held tight in my arms my beautiful baby, Scarlett. Sandra had her bath, the midwives left and we went to bed with our daughter lying between us; I could not wait for her older brother see her.

Three hours later I went to collect Jacob and told him that mummy had had a little girl and he had a baby sister. He was so excited, he ran to the car straight away and when we arrived home he ran upstairs gave his mummy a kiss. He lay down at the side of his sister, said, 'Hello', and kissed her on her cheek.

Childbirth is a phenomenal experience for a father and both of mine were special. I can only be grateful to Sandra for being so strong, so positive and so confident in everything we did. However, I will never forget the day I caught my daughter as she delivered in our own home.

Catherine's story (Sister)

I can't remember what woke me up the morning the baby was born. It might have been the many journeys up and down stairs, or the anxious cups of tea being made. Some time between 2 and 6am though, my brother, sisters and I all woke expectantly. I was 18; it was my last summer at home before I went to university in September. My sisters were 16 and 10, my brother was 14. When Mum first suggested a homebirth, we were horrified. My sister and I refused to be in the house when my Mum went into labour. It felt as though something secret and powerful would be brought right into our living room, something precious that would be cheapened by its domestic surroundings.

There was a lot of waiting that morning. As each one of the children woke up and came to investigate, we were reassured by Mum's sense of purpose and control. Mum seemed to know what to do to give birth. There was something instinctive about her movements, that she seemed to be in charge. She was restless, walking up and down stairs, rocking in a chair, seeking out a new place to be.

At times, I remember, we sat round talking and drinking tea. We all slipped in and out of reading, talking to Mum, listening from the top of stairs. Mum too slipped in and out of conversations. We could see her attention moving from us to her body, breathing heavily. She was still and focused, keeping her pain very private. But she came back, recovering herself between contractions. When she sat for too long though, she felt the contractions slowing down. She set off up and down the stairs again, trying to spur the birth along.

Dad was a quiet and nervous presence. For months he had been gathering apricot cereal bars as an emergency supply after reading they were good for women in labour. In the event, I don't think Mum wanted any, although my brother, sisters and I may have borrowed a few. We took our lead from him, learning when to distract Mum, and when to leave her. He looked on her struggle with the same respect I felt, trusting her to make it right.

The midwife was called before dawn. When I went to watch for her, I realised how early it was. The street was silent and dark. All of a sudden I was reminded of going on holiday as a child; setting off in the half-light before any of the neighbours were awake. It was strange to think of them asleep, unaware of the event which was rolling towards us. I wonder now if the reason Mum was so quiet and controlled was that she did not want to wake the neighbours with unexpected noises.

The midwife arrived and broke the spell of reverence which had been lingering over us. She knew what was happening, she had seen this before and knew what was supposed to happen next. She was friendly, but she had an air of unchallengeable authority about her. When she arrived, my siblings and I slunk off; it didn't seem right to be watching any more. Unsure of what our role was, we began to sit in other rooms and feign distance from it all.

It didn't last long though. I felt like I couldn't take my eyes off Mum. Gradually my mother was sinking deeper into herself, and along a journey that we couldn't follow. I was fascinated by her calmness and her confidence. She seemed to have her eyes clearly set on the end of this journey and she knew she had to steer herself there.

If the midwife was put off by having so many observers, she didn't show it. She showed my dad and I how to rub Mum's back to help her. The baby was coming out back to back, and as he turned it was hurting Mum. As the pain got worse, I began to feel afraid. It felt as though there was nothing we could do to help. It seemed as though we were all watching a horse heading full throttle towards a jump. Watching her thundering towards the inevitable, we were afraid that at the last minute she might realise the absurdity of what she was being asked to do, and turn her head and refuse the jump.

The midwife offered gas and air and I carried on rubbing Mum's back as she inhaled it. We were standing in her room, Mum resting on the chest of drawers. At first, I was pleased that there was something which might make it easier. My mother very quickly became someone else on the gas and air. Her arms went floppy, she was finding it harder to stand and was wobbling drunkenly. She muttered things I didn't understand and giggled. I was frightened. Mum's sense of purpose seemed to have disappeared; I didn't know if she even knew what she was doing. I had never before seen my mother out of control. Mum was always the one who held things together, who protected us and made everything okay. It was terrifying to see her like this. I felt as though my mother had abandoned me. Now I wonder how she spent so much of the labour protecting us, behaving normally, maintaining control. She put her children's need for normality above her desire to scream and shout and be looked after. Until the very last moments, I realise, she had been looking after us.

Another midwife arrived and we knew that it was nearly time. My sisters and my Dad were all in the room with Mum. I went to find my brother, not wanting him to be the only one who wasn't there. It seemed important, after so much waiting, to be ready to see the baby when he was born. He followed me to Mum's room, without a word.

When we returned, the midwife was kneeling beside Mum. She told us we could see the head. I had the biggest shock when, expecting to see the top of a baby's head, perhaps a tuft of hair, we saw his whole head emerge. All of his features, his eyes, nose, and mouth were all squashed into a tight rectangle in the middle of his huge face. I couldn't stop thinking that the baby's face, which would soon be so familiar, looked so mysterious.

When the baby was born, Mum sat down heavily on the bed. My youngest sister had brought warm towels, and the baby was wrapped in them, and passed to Mum. I found my camera on the chest of drawers, and took one picture. It seemed as though they had been reunited after a long traumatic separation.

The baby was passed around, to my Dad and siblings. I don't remember holding him, because Mum became shaky and cold. She looked pale and confused. Before she could get any rest, the midwife wanted her to deliver the placenta. It seemed so cruel that she couldn't join in with admiring the baby and being congratulated. My sister and I sat her up on the bed, supporting her back while she summoned the effort to do the next bit. She was exhausted. All we wanted to do was to tuck her into bed and take care of her. Obediently, she delivered the placenta before climbing into bed.

By this time, James, as he was to be called, had been cleaned and dressed. He was given to Mum, who looked him over admiringly, touching the creases in his neck and the small tufts of hair.

It was past 10 o'clock in the morning. The midwives left and we wandered our separate ways, to have breakfast and get dressed. For the rest of the day, I kept checking in on Mum and James, trying to make that night's events seem real.

Alison's story (Sister)

I was four years old when my brother Gregory was born. That night, I went into hospital with my mum, my dad and Claire (my cousin who was 21). I passed my mum face cloths and we talked together. We only had a midwife for a few minutes before. When it got close to his birth, a midwife said, 'Should she still be here?' That made me think something horrible was going to happen. I felt then that I shouldn't be there. I started to cry and went to the toy room with my cousin, thinking that children weren't meant to be allowed in the hospital. At the moment he was born, I was still crying and playing with toy eggs. I did this half-heartedly because I was worried about my mum. Minutes later, I came back into the room and saw my brother. I was relieved but still sobbing. I stroked his face and said, "I like it!"

Three years later, my sister was born. My mum and dad decided to have Sally at home in a birthing pool. They made this choice knowing we would have at least one midwife with us throughout. Three weeks before she was born, I remember ironing sheets with my mum. I was excited to be having a baby in the house again. I made my mum and dad promise me they would wake me up for the birth because I felt I had missed out on a big event when Gregory was born. Also, I made them promise to let me find out the gender myself. I didn't want anyone to spoil the surprise.

The night she was born we were playing 'Miss Polly had a dolly', acting out the nursery rhyme. I got out all my dollies and the toy telephone to ring the doctor. We all went to bed. Two and a half hours later, Claire woke me up (actually, she had to drag me down the stairs asleep) I'd just about opened my eyes when Sally was born. I felt happy that I hadn't missed out this time. I was delighted to meet her. I made platefuls of toast and lots of tea (my mum had five cups). The midwives said they wanted to take me with them! Once we'd all had a cuddle and a celebration with Babycham, we all just went back to sleep in our own beds. As soon as we got up in the morning we were all a bit giddy and got ready in our own time. We were relaxed, and happy to show our new arrival to visitors. I named Sally after Sally Snake in a book I'd read.

Another three years later, when I was 10, my second sister Tessa was born. Because Sally's birth had been so successful, my mum and dad wanted the same again (although my mum was worried that Sally's birth was so good that it couldn't be matched). Tessa Trickster had us all fooled, we thought she was transverse which would have meant a planned caesarean section. I was worried that this might mean there were complications. When I'd had a feel, I thought I could feel the feet near mum's ribs and that's just what the scan showed (I wonder if she'll be such a trickster when she's older). So, back to Plan A, a homebirth.

The night she was born, my dad, Greg and I went to a football match and my mum was looking round a high school for me. Just after the whistle was blown to start the match, my dad got a message from my cousin Claire (who had taken my mum) to say my mum's waters had broken. The rushing home made me worried and I really wanted to see my mum. As soon as I opened the door, I was suddenly very nervous about seeing her, but I went up to see her as she was just about to get in the bath. She looked normal, happy and cheery. I felt relieved and went down and got her some hot chocolate from the flask we'd taken to the football (it hadn't been touched on the match). Mum got in the bath and she seemed fine. After about an hour, she got out and sat downstairs for a bit. I sorted out her candles, music and pictures. Greg made me put 'Lily the Pink' on my CD player three times. He fell asleep in the chair soon after. Three hours after getting out of the bath, my mum got in the pool. She didn't seem to be in pain but the contractions were getting stronger. My dad had been rubbing her back and I'd done a bit to give him a rest. The midwives were chatting to me as well, not just the grown-ups. It wasn't as if they didn't like me being there. Mum was in the pool for half an hour. We were chatting and there were no awkward silences. It wasn't hurting mum that much. I was happy and I wanted to meet the baby.

She came out really fast. I'd just been chatting to Claire and then suddenly the baby was born. I had to jump out of the way because the midwife dived in to catch her. Everybody was ok. I made cups of tea but nobody ate the toast because they were too excited. After mum and dad had had a cuddle, I had some skin-to-skin contact with the baby. She was all soft and I was really happy to meet her. We got the day off school because we'd been up all night, but we went to the school mass and I showed her to all my friends. I felt proud. Then we went home and had lots of visitors.

Seeing childbirth has made me feel it's not a bad thing and it isn't scary. It made me think that I won't be screaming and that I will cope if I ever have any children.

CHAPTER 10

Tales from grandparents

Libby's story

Parenting and grand-parenting are inextricably intertwined and yet poles apart. Parenting seems a natural progression of adulthood, grand-parenting an absolute privilege.

Being a mother for me is hard and I've done it on my own for over 20 years. You care for your children when they're young only to come home one day and find they're gone, and all you're left with is an attic full of stuff that doesn't belong to you. Now, sometimes when I come home I gasp at the mess until I realise that one of them has come to visit. I put the phone down and realise that I'll always be someone's mum.

Parenting is anathema to me. I did it in my twenties and my daughter followed suit. I was considered old, she, young. Being a mother impinges on my life and every single decision that I've ever made. I take on my children's worries and problems as well as my own and I often despair at my inability to kiss it better. I lose sleep in the hope that they find sound slumber. But it's a decision I have never regretted and crow about my children to any poor friend or stranger who will listen, much to my children's chagrin, ask my son about his graduation. I wanted my children to understand conformity is not something to aspire to, but to occasionally accept. When I sang, pushing my trolley around the supermarket, my children would scatter. Now they join in. We do the traffic-light dance just to see other people smile.

I had no role models to be a parent or grandparent, other than a truth in my very being that childhood needs bucket loads of love, security and safety. I rather fancied I'd inflict that on my children but I think I failed on a couple of occasions. They have forgiven me.

Then I heard about Jenny. Her mother introduced us before she was born. I had no notion of the sheer impact becoming a Nana would have upon my very existence. Jenny's mum was not in the best of places when she chose her but she was as welcome and as cherished as any baby could wish for.

My daughter chose to have her baby in the safety of her home and I chose the only midwife I knew who could look after both of my girls. I was not my daughter's midwife, that was not my role, nor did I want to be. I have a strong personality and an almost militant attitude to the role midwives have in caring for women. My daughter had already listened to my endless ravings about feminism, misogyny and all things global. She had read my books when I undertook my midwifery education and she, being her mother's daughter, did herself proud.

Jenny decided to meet us all on a calm spring day. I have given endless thanks to the midwife that swapped her shift so I could be with my daughter, and the timeline that came together that day to make it all possible. Karma at its most shiny.

Jenny's mum gave birth to her daughter resting on my lap and who, like all knowing women, made her way quickly and quietly into her mother's arms. The last hour of her labour was hard fought and still makes me feel so excessively proud of her. I reached down and touched that little scrap of person just a fleeting moment after her mother.

I think it happened then, that proverbial truck blindsided me and struck me smack in the heart. I remember trying not to breathe so I could hang on to that moment for the longest time. The house was full of people and there were just the three of us. I sat very still, not wanting to interfere with that most precious moment. My daughter healed from a hurt I didn't even know existed and she became a new person. Jenny was responsible for making me new too.

She was tiny. The scales said she was an average baby, but she was slight. We didn't put her down; we didn't want to; it didn't seem fair to leave such a small soul on her own. She rested and was nurtured at her mother's breast and I held her against my chest, where we sank together in blissful calm and a peace that was earthy and basic.

I discovered a new emotion. I can't give it a name or even describe how it feels but it's overpowering. It would be very easy to be another parent for Jenny. I worked and still work very hard at not being the overbearing mother I had often been with my own children and am often gently reminded by those around me that see it and know how much hurt I could cause myself. Mothering was stressful, immeasurably complicated, rooted in guilt and I often did little more that get through the day. When my children moved on to school, I was relieved at the small amount of time I had to myself. I immersed myself in their child lives, becoming a school governor, seeking out opportunities to expand their lives and experiences and supporting them whenever and wherever I could, but that time on my own was mine.

When it suddenly dawned on me that Jenny was heading towards school, I panicked and was shocked at the power of that emotion. It meant really letting go to what small control I had over her life. Exposing her to beliefs, experiences and people that I would otherwise have vetoed because of my narrow-mindedness and judgemental attitude, even though I knew how great the detriment would be to her. But that was nothing to do with me. I let go and never let anyone know just how hard it was. Of course, she loves all her new friends, and her mother and I are joyous at her confidence and how unfazed she is by such a big change in her life.

I remember the day she first recognised me and realised I was one of her loved ones; the time she cried because I couldn't see her that day; every time she asks, 'I go your house, Nana?' and each and every time she stops when we are walking together, looks up at me and tells me she loves me, my heart bursts apart with utter disbelief. That tiny girl trusts me and loves me more than I feel I deserve.

When Jenny was three, Kitty decided to become her sister and, boy, did that polarise things for me even more. Kitty was born in the same house and the same room as her sister. She emerged fast and furious, planted both feet firmly in the roots of her family and made me face up to my obsession with trying to become a perfect nana. Jenny watched her sister being born with keen interest and I became an outsider. This of course, was entirely my problem and not the fault or design of anyone else. With consideration, my role is that of extended family, with a nuclear twist of course.

Kitty grounded me. She's an earthy baby. Rooted in security and the knowledge that all those that surround her have done it before. She thrives on the absolute lack of fanatic parenting that so often besets an older sibling. She forces me to back off by just being. She, like her sister, is just so very happy. It's incredibly easy to make her smile, that great big smile of hers, and she is loved, loved, loved. She makes me stop and consider my relationship with Jenny and I'm hoping one day Kitty too will gaze up at me and make me feel as humble as Jenny does.

I'm learning to let my love run free and with abandon; no conditions, no worrying, just loving because I can, because they demand it from me and because I just have so much to engulf them with. There are no trade-offs, and no hidden agendas.

I cannot heal my parenting mistakes by trying to create a perfect world for my granddaughters, nor should I try. I don't have anything to prove any more or fret because I got it wrong again. I'm learning to say sorry and I'm learning to let go.

But most important of all, I'm learning to be loved.

Marilyn's story

We sat at the dinner table after a fabulous meal cooked by Mary and Matthew then they announced that they had some news – they would be having a baby, due at the beginning of December 2006. Her father and I were absolutely thrilled at the thought of becoming grandparents; I'd secretly been looking forward to this announcement for months.

Their relationship of 12 years had resulted in a wonderful family wedding two years earlier. It was bound to happen sooner rather than later. Tony and I were living in London at the time but there was no way I was going to be separated from this most exciting turn of events by 230 miles. The tenants were served notice and we moved back into the family home a month before the expected event. Mary and Matthew had done their research and they'd both worked at getting their bodies into the best shape for planning a baby. The optimal time for the birth had been calculated and fortunately things had gone pretty much to plan. We sat back in eager anticipation for our newest member of the family to arrive. Mary blossomed and all went well with the pregnancy. Both my pregnancies had gone fine with no complications; both girls born two to three days before their due date in midwife-led units. My mother, sister and niece had followed similar patterns.

I fully expected Mary to follow in the same tradition. All planning was in hand, we duly sat back to wait for baby to make his/her appearance. Then it hit me like a being whacked by a cricket bat, my girl was going to have to go through a labour, my child who we'd spent 30 years nurturing and protecting, was going to have to go through that ancient ritual of women throughout the ages. I didn't want my girl to have to go through that, although at the same time I did. It's another rite of passage to being a women, shared with millions and millions of other women throughout the centuries since life began. It's a life-changing experience that you never forget, even after 30 years, it unites us women; it's part of what bonds us together.

I wanted my daughter's care to be the best, second to none. I wanted my grandchild to be brought into the world with the least trauma and as naturally as possible with as little medical intervention as possible, on Mary and Matthew's terms not on some timetable dictated by an obstetrician or by a shortage of beds or facilities. From what I had heard, labour had been turned into some kind of battery hen experience with fund managers deciding policy on pounds per delivery or so it had sounded. I wanted my daughter's baby to make his appearance when he was ready and in his own time. I also wanted her labour to be monitored from a distance by professional midwives experienced in doing their job.

No two women are the same, no labour is 'average' or 'normal', deliveries vary even within the same woman. No two women have the same labours; they are individuals and should be treated as such. In most cases nature sorts out the birth process in its own good time. Pregnancy is not an illness. It's life in the raw. What women experience at that time affects them for life, those experiences, positive or negative, affect how they bond with their children and cope with their family. They have to be as empowering as possible. Our grandchild will be nurtured and watched, held safe as he makes his way through his life, not mine, not his parents, his.

Events didn't go to the 'birthing plan' but the result was still just as fantastic and positive. Mary's blood pressure started to rise as the days past her due date mounted. The last thing she'd wanted was to be induced and her midwife did her best to avoid this but it was finally decided that this had to be the way forward. Waters were broken by the midwife after a failed attempt by the doctor on duty. We all know that inducing brings on powerful contractions very quickly. Matt did his best to keep us informed on her progress but it's difficult while trying to be there for your wife. A point was reached when Mary thought she'd had enough without pain relief, fortunately Matt remembered what a wise midwife had said at one of their antenatal classes, if you felt like this, try to give it another 20 minutes before doing anything. That worked; Mary duly moved on to the final stage. Within a very short time George was born.

Meanwhile, at home, Tony and I had gone to bed trying to relax and get some sleep. Later we worked out that just as the contractions had started to take their toll on the mum to be, nan to be started having very sharp low abdominal pains. I knew instinctively that the birth was imminent and sure enough we got the (for me) emotional call to say our grandson was born, mum had been brilliant and both were well. Those pains I'd felt proved to me that the mother and child bond is for life no matter how far apart you are.

What a lot of fun we're going to have over the years, I can't wait. He's a long-term project. Just as with my own children the love you feel instantly for a grandchild is the same deep and unconditional love you feel for your own children.

Juliet's story

When I was asked by my daughter Hannah to be a birth partner at the birth of her first baby I was thrilled. Having lost my husband six months before, this was a very difficult time. To have the privilege of being present when new life was coming into the family was very special.

Hannah is also a midwife and so had a very strong idea of how she wanted her birthing experience to be. She is quite tiny and towards the end of her pregnancy the team of midwives caring for her were not happy with her wish to have a homebirth, and had an idea that Hannah might be having a very small baby. Hannah reluctantly had a couple of scans for the sake of the team so that they might have more confidence in her decision. Eventually they agreed to her opting for the homebirth experience.

I live a four hour car journey away from Hannah and so we were both a little anxious about my arriving on time. However, in the event, the day after Hannah's due date, she tearfully phoned me up and I decided to make the journey even though she was not yet in labour. I was anxious for her, and she was obviously reaching an emotional time. In fact we only had to wait one day after my arrival for her to commence her labour.

She had a fairly long pre-labour stage starting in the early hours of the morning. I awoke to the sound of the bath being run and was then aware that something was happening. Hannah's husband Rob and I then began our task of supporting her according to her instructions. Mid-morning Rob went out for some provisions and came home with a lovely bunch of flowers for his expectant wife. During this time Hannah was dealing with contractions and pain.

She had asked her cousin Anna, also a young midwife, to be another birthing partner. Anna arrived mid-morning and we were all excited at the forthcoming prospect. Hannah and Anna, who have a similar philosophy, shared many beautiful moments, swaying and dancing as Hannah's pains came and went. We took it in turns to do some back massage and had Classic FM playing on the radio to keep us all in a relaxed mood. Hannah seemed to want to move from room to room, and upstairs as well as downstairs. We just did whatever she wanted.

At some stage Rob filled the birthing pool which was in the kitchen. This seemed to take a long time, but did prove to be of enormous benefit to Hannah to help her deal with her contractions.

During this time she seemed to come and go in her own world, and seemed very serene, even through her contractions. The scene was almost spiritual. The midwife arrived early evening when Hannah decided it was time to call her, and then she took over the monitoring, etc. As she reached the final stage of labour both Rob and I were a little anxious. Kim, the midwife, wanted Hannah to come out of the pool as I think she felt she could monitor the situation better. Hannah gave birth to Thomas in the front room at about 9.30pm. The fire was lit, the curtains drawn on this February evening, it was snowing gently outside. When they put Thomas on Hannah before he was weighed the whole scene was so beautiful, and Hannah was so fulfilled. I remember feeling amazed at the whole experience and so proud of Hannah. She had remained in control and had given birth to a healthy little 7lb 10oz boy, not a small baby at all. She was very content. Rob was then invited to have skin to skin contact with the new baby.

Although I have had three successful labours myself, I found the experience of watching my last child deliver her own baby incredibly moving. Nothing like the conveyor belt experiences I had those many years ago when everything was controlled by the hospital and I didn't seem to have any say in what was happening.

Sheena's story:

Part I

Holland, 3.35am, August 31st 2008: 'Contractions every 10 minutes for an hour, now on our way in. Here he comes!'

As I begin to write this story, my son James' wife Daphne is in labour with their second child, in Holland. They know the sex of their baby, it is a boy, but have never revealed his chosen name. We are travelling home from holidaying in Portugal; it is also my sister's birthday. I received the text message above on my mobile phone, and gently whispered to my sleeping husband, 'Daphne's in labour' and then I lay and thought about what was happening to her, and prayed.

Minnie will meet her new brother today, and family and friends from England, The Netherlands and many other countries, are desperate for this boy child to be born safely and to see his face for the first time. My mind is concentrating on Daphne, her labour, that hard time, and the struggle she had when Minnie was born. Minnie arrived by caesarian section, after a long difficult labour; we (my husband Paul and I) didn't arrive until after her birth.

James and Daphne were totally happy with Minnie's birth; they were over the moon with their baby girl and it was evident that they felt like triumphant parents. Daphne was strong and sure with her ability to parent and nurture this new life, and I beheld my son for the first time, in love with his child as I was with him, and emotions were rekindled as I stood and watched, in awe and with so much pride. James is my second child, my first a girl, so his growing new family is taking the same shape as mine. I think about James' birth and when we first met; a contrast to my first birth, much easier in effort, and different in experience. Will James be thinking of this when he supports and loves Daphne through the birth, until the time they meet their son?

Another message arrives on my mobile phone: 'D doing well, her mum with her now, I am going back shortly.'

And now we wait. He is coming. I feel anxious and excited all at the same time, how long now?

When the baby is six days old, we meet the beautiful boy for the first time. How amazing this little family is! Quentin is already a family member, and Minne is happy to accept him into the fold. James has already told us that again the birth was difficult, and Daphne confirms that. They wonder why it was so hard, when, they tell me, Daphne's mother had babies so easily. I am not sure, but I remember feeling the same when my daughter had difficulties birthing her son, when for me it was straightforward.

James tells me all about how difficult he found seeing the birth, and wasn't sure whether it's a good thing men being in the birthing room. I have to agree that I understand his reasoning, but would he feel happy missing that special moment? He tells me about his intense love for Minnie, and wonders if he'll ever feel the same for Quentin?

'Of course' I say. 'Father and son, think about your own dad.'

Part 2

Tomorrow, Seamus will be three. He came to us in a flurry of apprehension, after Anna, my daughter, had so wonderfully and courageously laboured in our kitchen, in a water pool, for many hours.

I saw my husband Paul quietly supporting the care of his first born girl, and supporting Shaun her partner. I didn't expect him to be at all involved, and yet it felt right that he was there, in the background. My strong wonderful girl tried so hard to birth this boy naturally, but it wasn't to be; Seamus was going to come in style, demanding attention from the very beginning.

During my daughter's pregnancy I felt sure and confident that she would share the same experience of birth as I had, as my mother had, and as her mother had before her. I know that mothers and daughters more often than not share similar labours and births, and so sure was I that this would be so for Anna that I wrote an article detailing the reasons for my certainty (Byrom, 2005). I experienced an incredible thrill and surge of love as my child carried a child. I felt so proud of her coping mechanism and energy, and wondered if my mother had felt this about me. Anna asked me many questions, even though she was a midwife herself. Her questions were about personal things, about nurture and delight.

When Seamus was born, I spent days with my daughter that I will hold in my heart forever. She needed me by her side as she breast fed her little man and fought off over-cautious medical teams. We bonded further, the three of us, and I tried to support this new little family as they familiarised themselves with each other at the beginning of their own special journey.

References

Byrom S (2005) Mothering the mother, midwife and baby: A personal account. *British Journal of Midwifery* **13**(10): 621

CHAPTER 11

Tales of unusual births

Anita's story (Midwife)

I met Natalie approximately 16 weeks into her second pregnancy, when she was referred to me for caseload midwifery care. Natalie had been booked for her maternity care, and at her first appointment with the consultant obstetrician she had asked for an elective caesarean section, giving the reason that she could not go through a birth experience like she had had with her first baby. The consultant suggested that Natalie meet with the consultant midwife to discuss her concerns in more detail. Natalie agreed to this, and following a lengthy discussion, it was thought that Natalie might benefit from the caseload model of care with a named midwife who could work with her throughout the pregnancy, and provide intrapartum care.

I arranged to see Natalie at home for our first meeting. It was an emotional meeting as she described her first birth experience to me, and hence the reason she was now requesting a caesarean section. She had pre-labour rupture of membranes at term, was kept in hospital, and told that she would need to be induced after 24 hours if labour did not start.

Natalie told me, 'I was sure that if I was left a little longer, I knew I would go on my own. I was made to feel like an irresponsible parent, putting the life of my unborn child at risk by not complying with hospital policy, i.e. induction after 24 hours. I foolishly went along with agreeing to the induction despite not really believing it was the right thing to do.'

She did not feel well-supported and described an incident during her labour where 'a fetal probe monitor (fetal scalp electrode) was suggested and I refused it so the senior midwife came in to "bully" me into agreeing to it. I didn't.'

Natalie described in powerful detail how she felt about the birth: 'I had a long second stage and didn't progress. My contractions were irregular and not lasting long enough to push with. Two obstetricians came into the room and with very little explanation, I was put on my back, catheterised, had an episiotomy and a ventouse delivery. My episiotomy extended into a third degree tear. The whole situation was handled very badly with poor communication with me or my husband. I wasn't supported well enough by the staff and I was 'made' to go along with what suited their needs, not mine. I felt powerless. I wish I hadn't agreed to the induction. I felt let down by the hospital and I felt I let myself down too by not being strong (and I usually am). I felt like I'd let Chloe down by allowing her to be born in such a way. I felt like I'd failed. I wanted a waterbirth or as natural a delivery as possible. In a way, the staff's attitude to mums wanting a natural delivery was almost laughed at. I felt traumatised by the whole thing. It felt like butchery. I wasn't supported post-delivery either. My sutures fell out, the wound opened, I got an infection and it all took months to heal properly. Psychologically, I couldn't cope with what had happened to me and my sex life didn't resume properly for almost 18 months. It had a serious effect on my relationship with my husband. There was no support from the hospital and the GP was less than helpful. I swore I'd never have another child because I couldn't cope with being pregnant or giving birth, not to mention how if affected your feelings about your spouse. The thought of it made me feel physically sick. I had flash-backs about the birth and nightmares where I was re-living it. I can remember details about it and the level of pain. The memory didn't fade.'

Natalie described feeling devastated when she found out she was pregnant for a second time.

'I was absolutely petrified. I cried every day for about a fortnight. I thought about having a termination, I'm ashamed to say that now that David's here and he's beautiful, but I did. When I did the pregnancy test and saw the positive result, I can't describe the terrible feeling I had in the pit of my stomach. Straight away, I thought, "How the hell am I going to get this baby out without the carnage that I had last time?"'

Despite this first meeting being very difficult and emotional for Natalie, it enabled me to understand her feelings and fears about the birth. She was initially concerned that I was there to try to persuade her to have a normal birth. However, I was soon able to reassure her that I was there to help and would support her in her choices, whatever they might be. I advised Natalie that she did not need to worry about making a decision about the mode of birth until much later on in the pregnancy, and during this time we would be able to discuss at length what we could do differently to avoid a repeat of the first experience, and to explore the available information and evidence to enable her to make fully informed choices.

She was happy to do this, and over the coming months, this is exactly what happened. By 36 weeks, Natalie and I had developed a relationship built on trust and mutual respect. She was much more confident and now desperately wanted to have a normal birth, although she still had some serious reservations. She wasn't afraid of labour or giving birth, but she was afraid of medical intervention if things didn't go according to plan. She wanted to try for a normal birth, but she needed reassurance that her wishes and choices would be supported, and she would not be forced into anything she wasn't happy with. Her partner, Simon, was keen to support her choices.

I suggested to Natalie that we go together to see a consultant obstetrician to discuss her choices and agree a plan that she would feel more confident with. She was a little unsure about seeing an obstetrician in case they tried to persuade her into doing something she didn't feel happy with, but I reassured her that I would be there with her as her advocate, and wouldn't let that happen. She therefore agreed, and was very glad that she did.

Induction wasn't an option for Natalie, under any circumstances. She felt that she would prefer to have a caesarean section if she had not given birth two weeks after her due date. Her other major fear was if she again failed to progress in the second stage of labour. She could not cope with the idea of having another instrumental birth, and would prefer to have a caesarean section than an instrumental delivery if the need arose. The consultant listened to Natalie, discussed her fears and wishes with her, and respected her choices. She agreed to Natalie's requests, and clearly documented the agreed plan in the case notes, so they would not be declined by an on-call registrar when the time came. Natalie came away from the consultation feeling empowered and in control. She felt she had been listened to, and had been fully involved in the decisions made.

Natalie started labour spontaneously a few days after her due date. She was calm, relaxed, and progressed quickly to the second stage. However, despite having strong, regular contractions with strong urges to push, and remaining upright and mobile, she once again had a long second stage without descent of the baby's head. At this point, I was very aware that Natalie was relying on me to be her advocate and to ensure the plan of care that had been put in place was adhered to. I was also aware how very disappointed Natalie would be to have come so far, then not have a normal birth. The on-call consultant obstetrician was on the delivery suite at the time, so I explained Natalie's story to her, and the plan she had agreed with her own consultant.

Natalie was kneeling up on a large mat on the floor, leaning over the bed, when the consultant came into the room. The doctor's kind and understanding approach soon put her at ease. She explained that she understood Natalie's fears, and asked permission to examine her to see what would be the best way to help her. Natalie appeared to panic at the thought of having to lie on the bed, but soon calmed when the doctor said she would be able to examine her in the kneeling position just where she was.

Following the examination, the doctor explained that she understood if Natalie wanted to go to theatre as expressed in her plan, but felt that if she applied forceps to bring the head down a little bit more, she would then be able to remove them, enabling Natalie to then push the baby out herself. Again, Natalie said that she just didn't feel that she could go onto the bed and into the lithotomy position without feeling panic, so the consultant agreed to try to apply the forceps with Natalie continuing to kneel up on the mat on the floor, leaning over the bed. She did this and brought the head down slightly, after which she removed the forceps. Natalie then described having an overpowering urge to bear down, far stronger than she had experienced previously, and very soon pushed her baby out.

She later described to me that had felt safe and in control because she believed that the doctor truly understood and respected her fears and her wishes, and she also had confidence that I wouldn't let anything awful happen to her again.

'I was even OK with the fact that the doctor had to use the forceps to just edge David around my "U-bend" where he was a bit stuck. I was just grateful that she agreed to lie down on the floor to do it rather than make me lie on my back – I'd have completely freaked if I'd had to do that. I'm convinced that because she did that, i.e. lay down underneath me, I avoided an episiotomy and lots more psychological trauma.'

My own feelings and thoughts reflected those of Natalie. I also trusted and had confidence in the doctor, in the way she treated and communicated with Natalie, Simon and myself, and because I had come to know Natalie so well, I knew she felt safe in going along with the doctor's suggestion. I felt, at the time, that we were all working together as a united team, with Natalie's needs central to every shared decision.

Natalie was thrilled with her birth experience and described feeling 'over the moon'. She later said that although she couldn't forget her first birth, it now didn't seem so bad because she felt that she'd had some resolution to it through this second experience, and it had enabled her to move on in a way she hadn't felt able to before.

This story could easily have concluded with Natalie having a caesarean section, but instead it demonstrates that, with suitable support and advocacy, women may be empowered to feel safe and in control of their birth experiences. The progress of both of Natalie's labours were actually quite similar, but because of the support she received, and the way she felt she was treated, they appeared to her to be two very contrasting experiences. A potentially very 'abnormal' labour became as 'normal' as possible, having a huge impact on how Natalie perceived her labour, and on her health and well-being afterwards.

CHAPTER 12

Tales from the labour ward

Sheena, Kirsten, Sarah, Sue:
The Birthday Theatre Group

The Birth Day Theatre is a group of mothers who came together because of a common issue; they had all experienced a traumatic birth experience (Byrom et al, 2007). Their first meeting was cathartic and profound, and was the beginning of a continuing momentous journey. The women are passionate in their aim to influence positively the attitudes of caregivers, and to refocus maternity service provision. They do this through acting out 'stories', stories that they have told and retold, and through deep and nurturing connections with each other, and two midwives.

The role of these midwives, in common with so much midwifery practice, was to create a safe space for people to do difficult things. The development of the group was an emotional wave, it was long, and had periods of rushes and calms. As our medium was drama, the work was physical as well as verbal, and this often triggered a re-emergence of long-buried feelings. In one particularly poignant preparation session, we used the metaphor of masks to explore how these feelings are concealed beneath a veneer of acceptable 'coping' behaviour, striking deep chords with the group.

Turning private and often hidden experiences into a public performance was a key element in the success of this story. It was important to work with an outside eye, and playwright Mary Cooper crafted the material we had generated and recorded, giving it shape and an accessible narrative form. So, our play '*Speech to Rita*' was born, emerging after much physical and emotional effort, supported and nurtured by craftswomen. It is a timely and articulate story which represents both personal growth and political influence, as witnessed by responses from performers and audiences. Sarah, one of the women who formed the group following the birth of her second child, provides an insight of what this means to her.

Sarah's story

My experience is typical in that the trauma of my first birth was resurrected with the news of my second pregnancy. After my first child was born, I tried to hide my battered emotions. I didn't want to be a bad mother, I wanted to cope. I cried daily for months and months. But life had to go on. Moving house, and therefore coming under a different hospital, played a part in my being able to go ahead with another pregnancy. However, I was truly terrified of the reality of having to give birth again. Thankfully this was appreciated by a midwife who really did change my life. She showed me a way through the anguish, and gave me the strength and courage that I needed to have to cope successfully with giving birth again. And I did a magnificent job!

This midwife asked me to go along to a discussion group on traumatic birth. I had long shared the heartbreak of anyone who had experienced a traumatic birth, but having to sit in a room with other women, and hear them verbalise their own painful experiences made me angry. I wanted to have a voice that would be heard where it counted. I wanted to shout out, kick up a fuss, change attitudes. And I wasn't alone. So the Birth Day Theatre Group was formed.

I am so proud to be a part of Birth Day. My fellow actors are women, who, like me, have their own experiences of traumatic birth, and their own reasons for taking part – but we share the goal of making a change for the better in midwifery practice. There were seven of us in the beginning, all of us mothers with experiences of both positive and traumatic birth. We don't get to meet up very often because of work and family commitments. Indeed our first performance was given after only eight meetings. But that alone shows how well we have been able to come together as individuals, and become a team with a powerful bond. I am fiercely proud of us and of what we do. We have shared laughter and many, many tears. We have swapped intimate details and yet I have only just learnt everyone's surname! Because those little details don't matter. What does matter is what we feel inside and care about deeply, and that is for women to have the proper support and care they need when giving birth. It matters that they are allowed to make well-informed choices, and be treated with respect. We have all made very great personal emotional sacrifices to do this, but have so far been rewarded with appreciative and responsive audiences. And best of all – we have found each other.

The rehearsals for the piece of theatre took months, almost a year. When the time came to perform for an audience, emotions returned strongly.

Sue's account

We travelled early morning – full of nerves and that. Listened to a few talks and then we really needed to get together as a group for a couple of hours. Did several rehearsals that day – in the gardens, in the bedroom, in pairs and as a group. I actually felt 'faint' just before we started, but quickly relaxed and actually enjoyed performing in front of around 160 delegates! Everything went well. We did it! It felt so good, I can't explain. We expected positive feedback I think – but we were all overwhelmed by the 'sea of hands' – people eager to comment and praise, followed by direct feedback later from people. Words like 'powerful', 'must be shown at a higher level', 'emotional', 'real to life' were but a few. I think we were really overcome and so happy at the resulting words from the audience, we were buzzing. The next day was surreal and I felt I needed to do it again – soon – it was just so brilliant, so big, so what we wanted to happen.

Audiences have been varied, and throughout the UK, there have included service users, midwives, doctors, and supervisors of midwives. The response has been sometimes very encouraging and at other times challenging for the members, as beliefs are confronted. In the main however, the strength of their characters and the message behind their story, shone through.

Two student midwives detailed their thoughts: 'A very well-acted performance that really brings home the nature of midwifery from a woman's perspective, that often, as midwives, we fail to see, even though we are all women.'

'Thank you so much, you have helped me realise that despite all of the medical terminology, etc. involved in midwifery care, and the daunting prospect of qualifying I realise that what is really important is communication and being there for women.'

The future is always uncertain for the group, even though women's voices become stronger to challenge the systems of maternity care. But forever these women will remember their united strength, their passion and will to try to make things better for all those yet to be born.

References

Byrom S, Baker K, Broome C, Hall J (2007) Speech to Rita: The birth of a voice. *Practising Midwife* 10(1): 19–21

CHAPTER 13

Towards humanised maternity care

Sheena Byrom

There's nothing like a story. Whether a child or an adult, stories appeal to human beings and hold the potential to transport the listener or reader into the world of the teller. And whether the story tells a happy or sad tale, the sentiment can be felt. The stories in this book have described a range of intense emotions surrounding birth, and will potentially evoke a similar response in those who read them. These stories will be told and retold, and now not just by those who played a part in their making.

When I was younger, and being the youngest of five girls, my mother and sisters often spoke of their births. Their descriptions were not detailed, but were relayed to me in messages of 'work then pleasure', 'so painful but good'; something definitely worth doing and being excited for, so I anticipated the unknown without fear, and with the assurance that if the other females in my family had done it, so could I. Sometimes stories such as these are lost within families and communities, or replaced by tales of trauma and tragedy from media and film.

For the past six years, as part of my work, I have listened to birth stories, from strong women who, during a vulnerable time, needed to explore unanswered questions. The stories are not happy ones; they are sad and distressing. They are accounts of births told sometimes for the first time, vividly and emotionally, in an attempt to try to 'make things right'. I have never listened so closely before, never had the time, but the experience has given me the deepest insight into how birth potentially affects us all, and it has strengthened a personal passion to change things. However, the stories in this book, and many others too, are often joyous inspirational tales of triumph and love, where women and their partners are filled with a renewed force to begin their roles as parents.

My career as a midwife began with an extensive period working in a maternity home (GP unit). It was a sort of birth centre environment, where physiological childbirth with minimal intervention was the norm. With wonderful midwives I learnt to listen, feel and comprehend. I developed skills to confidently support women and their partners during labour and to facilitate beautiful moments of birth. It seemed at the time that all births were happy occasions, with women being free and unleashed to birth in the way they wanted to. Birth centres are frequently described as the perfect medium to support physiological birth (Kirkham, 2003; Walsh, 2007), and homebirth is associated with increased satisfaction rates (RCOG/RCM, 2007). Indeed the ripple effect from this can influence neighbourhoods.

One of my colleagues, Caroline Broome, recently told stories of how homebirth was influencing a change in a community in Lancashire where birth wasn't really a priority.

'What I think I meant was that rather than the birth process being an abstract, isolated occurrence, the local community seemed to have taken its role in supporting the family unit and became involved in the whole process. After the last birth I remember the woman saying that she didn't even know the family directly across the road after her first baby yet after her homebirth the first neighbour to visit with a gift was in fact this mother. Another told me that when she was filling her birthing pool she didn't have enough water pressure and the next door neighbour with whom she had little contact ran an extra hose-pipe from their tap, outside and into her house to fill the pool quicker. Isn't that fabulous. I met her on Friday in the chip shop and she was still raving about her birth (for everyone to hear while ordering chow mien!). It is almost as if the 'ownership' of the birth process shifts from the professionals to the community... I truly believe that this feeling of ownership brings an ethos of responsibility and therefore cohesion within the community where in a locality of high family breakdown, it actually brings feelings of support and integration for such families.'

Nonetheless, most births in the UK take place in hospital settings, and supportive, nurturing care is happening there too, as is evident in the stories in this book. But for positive stories from hospital birth to expand, we need to continue to listen hard to the women and their loved ones, and to take note. In *Chapter 10*, Grandmothers recounted memories of what it was like for them when they birthed their babies, in the 1970s and 1980s. We would be wise to take heed of warnings of too much interference and processing. Grandmothers won't always hold this viewpoint, as the next generation may have had little opportunity to feel strong and empowered during their birth experience.

The story of birth across the UK in particular has shifted. Very recently, this was demonstrated during several 'away time' sessions with senior midwives. As a warm up exercise, 40 or so midwives were invited to talk about their own birth, and to tell the tale of what it was like for their mothers when they were born. The ages of the midwives ranged from 35 to 50, and out of all the participants only two had been born via operative birth. Most were born at home, including triplets and a breech presentation. We know now that the results of the same exercise carried out in 30 years time will be significantly different.

Various available statistics highlight this phenomenon to us; since my days in the maternity home, intervention rates and consequential instrumental and operative birth rates have soared and continue to do so. The impact is that the workload has increased for maternity care workers. There is increased service costs for commissioners, and the only diminishing fact is the woman's confidence in her ability to birth her baby. So, as the stories change, several reasons are suggested as potential influences and include fear of litigation, societal beliefs influenced by media, maternity service provision, poorly developed clinical guidelines, 'pain free' labour and an inherent fear of the birth process.

In an interesting chapter on 'midwifery guardianship', Fahy et al (2008) suggest that women's knowledge of birth has been lost within Western societies, where only what can be seen and counted is considered real. The authors use a story to demonstrate the concept of power, and how it operates between the woman and her birth territory during labour. Many of the women I see describe this notion clearly, without perhaps fully understanding it. It is a script that is replayed to me time and time again: the woman's 'power' is lost during the birth of her baby, the baby is extracted and the whole process belongs to someone else.

So what can be done? To influence any change from the current situation, accounts of birth, both good and bad, need to be disseminated more widely, so those involved in care receive feedback as to how their actions influence events. In an attempt to achieve wider communication of stories, we tried using drama (*Chapter 12*) and research, exploring in depth the experiences of birth of 14 women (see *Chapter 6*). Women, midwives and obstetricians need to combine their energies to assist in the promotion of positive, physiological birth, although solutions seem difficult to find (Downe, 2008).

In the concluding chapter of her seminal book on the subject of normal birth, Soo Downe reiterates what Caroline Broome describes above, by briefly touching on the public health issues associated with birth (Downe, 2008), and suggesting the potential for increased social capital and community well-being when the birth experience is a positive one. The benefits of a positive birth story are profoundly important to society as a whole, and therefore the responsibility to influence humanised birth extends beyond caregivers and receivers, to include commissioners and service provider managers, in addition to politicians and policy makers. We hope this book is able to play a small part.

References

Byrom S, Baker K, Broome C, Hall J (2007) Speech to Rita: The birth of a voice. *Practising Midwife* 10(1): 19–21

Downe S (2008) Aspects of a controversy: Summary and debate. In: Downe S (Ed) *Normal Childbirth*. 2nd Edn. Churchill Livingstone Elsevier, London

Fahy K, Hastie C (2008) Midwifery guardianship: Reclaiming the sacred in birth. In Fahy K, Foureur M, Hastie C (Eds) *Birth Territory and Midwifery Guardianship*. Butterworth Heinemann Elsevier, Sydney

Kirkham M (2003) *Birth Centres: A Social Model for Maternity Care*. Elsevier Health Science

RCOG/RCM (2007) *Homebirth*. Joint statement No.2. Royal College of Obstetricians and Gynaecologists/Royal College of Midwives

Walsh D (2007) *Small is Beautiful: Lessons for Maternity Services From a Birth Centre*. Radcliffe Publishing, Oxford